FREDERICK LEONG, PH.D.
THE OHIO STATE UNIVERSITY
DEPARTMENT OF PSYCHOLOGY
142 TOWNSHEND HALL
1885 NEIL AVENUE MALL
COLUMBUS OHIO 43210-1222

Manpower for Mental Health

Modern Applications of Psychology

a series edited by

JOSEPH D. MATARAZZO

UNIVERSITY OF OREGON MEDICAL SCHOOL

Manpower for Mental Health

Edited by

FRANKLYN N. ARNHOFF,
ELI A. RUBINSTEIN, AND
JOSEPH C. SPEISMAN

ALDINE PUBLISHING COMPANY
Chicago

First published 1969 by Aldine Publishing Company, 529 South Wabash, Chicago, Illinois 60605

Library of Congress Catalog Card Number 68-8145
Designed by Chestnut House
PRINTED IN THE UNITED STATES OF AMERICA

Contributors

George W. Albee, Ph.D., is George Trumbull Ladd Professor of Psychology, Case Western Reserve University.

Franklyn N. Arnhoff, Ph.D., is Chief, Manpower and Analytic Studies Branch, Division of Manpower and Training Programs, National Institute of Mental Health.

Henry David, Ph.D., is Executive Secretary, Division of Behavioral Sciences, National Academy of Sciences–National Research Council.

Joan W. Jenkins, Ph.D., is Research Psychologist, Manpower and Analytic Studies Branch, Division of Manpower and Training Programs, National Institute of Mental Health.

Donald R. Jones, Ph.D., is Chief, Manpower Studies Section, Manpower and Analytic Studies Branch, Division of Manpower and Training Programs, National Institute of Mental Health.

Herbert E. Klarman, Ph.D., is Professor of Public Health Administration, School of Hygiene and Public Health, Johns Hopkins University.

Harold D. Lasswell, Ph.D., is Edward J. Phelps Professor of Law and Political Science, Yale Law School.

Alan D. Miller, M.D., is Commissioner, New York State Department of Mental Hygiene.

Anne Roe, Ph.D., is Professor Emerita, Harvard University.

Peter H. Rossi, Ph.D., is Chairman, Department of Social Relations, Johns Hopkins University.

Eli A. Rubinstein, Ph.D., Assistant Director for Extramural Programs and Behavioral Sciences, National Institute of Mental Health.

Beatrice M. Shriver, Ph.D., is Chief, Special Studies Section, Manpower and Analytic Studies Branch, Division of Manpower and Training Programs, National Institute of Mental Health.

Joseph C. Speisman, Ph.D., is Chairman, Department of Psychology, Boston University.

Philip Wexler, Ed.D., is Assistant Commissioner, Education and Training, New York State Department of Mental Hygiene.

Preface

INCREASINGLY in the past decade, mental health manpower has been an issue of major concern as one aspect of the national mental health program. The need for additional manpower to perform the variety of activities in growing programs has continued to be an important consideration in determining how rapidly progress can be made. While there has been a marked expansion in the total number of trained personnel in the mental health professions, the growth in these professions has been more than matched by the expanding needs of the total national mental health program.

Since the publication of the final report of the Joint Commission on Mental Illness and Health [1] in 1961, American society has changed considerably, as has the field of mental health. The development of community mental health centers and the broadened delivery of services to those in need have produced a new demand for a systematic reevaluation of the problems and issues of mental health manpower. As one part of such an assessment, the National Institute of Mental Health sponsored and conducted a symposium, "Manpower and Mental Health," at Airlie

---

1. *Action for mental health.* 1961. New York: Basic Books.

House, Warrenton, Virginia, June 28–30, 1967. This volume is based on the formal papers presented and the proceedings of the symposium.

The purpose of the meeting was to examine specific concepts and theoretical issues that are of importance in mental health manpower policy and in the further development of the entire mental health program. It was purposely concerned with issues that have significance for total program implementation, rather than being directed exclusively at manpower considerations and manpower shortages of the present moment.

Such conceptual considerations involve a knowledge and awareness of the composition, general patterns, and trends of the total labor force complex and how they relate to mental health manpower. Other considerations pertain to an awareness of the changes in the types of mental health manpower that will be needed in the future; trends in obsolescence and needs for retraining; recognition that shortages of manpower expressed in quantitative units and production of personnel are functions of utilization in that both depend on how and in what respects personnel are used.[2]

All of this requires a careful examination of the relationship of mental health manpower to the larger arena both within mental health and beyond. In essence, it is necessary to look at mental health manpower from a variety of perspectives before an adequate assessment can be made of where it is now, let alone where it should be in the future.

The participants were invited, not only because of their various specialties and expert knowledge, but also because of their different approaches to the issues involved in analysis of manpower problems. In order to permit the broadest possible discussion, some of the participants were invited as experts in their own disciplines despite the fact that they had not been identified previously with mental health manpower. The editors believe the symposium markedly benefited from this diversity of approach.

Following the symposium, each paper was revised and expanded, drawing upon the discussions and the comments of the discusssants. The editors are particularly grateful to the discussants, whose criticisms and comments were so helpful: Mary Jean Bowman, John K. Folger, Victor Howery, Mary F. Liston, Norton Long, and Benjamin Pasamanick.

The last chapter draws very heavily upon the formal comments made by the discussants as well as the general interchange, and has attempted to abstract and integrate the wealth of ideas that were presented. Any deficiencies in this regard are the responsibility of the authors of that chapter. The statements and opinions expressed throughout are those of the individual authors and do not necessarily reflect the policy or position of the Public Health Service.

---

2. National Institute of Mental Health. 1963. *A mental health manpower studies program*. Washington, D.C.: U.S. Government Printing Office.

Finally, the editors wish to express their appreciation to Laura Arnhoff for her unstinting assistance in bibliographic search, editing, and helpful criticisms.

F.N.A.

E.A.R.

J. C. S.

Contents

CHAPTER 1

The Mental Health Fields: An Overview of Manpower Growth and Development

FRANKLYN N. ARNHOFF,
ELI A. RUBINSTEIN,
BEATRICE M. SHRIVER, AND
DONALD R. JONES

THE HISTORY OF THE CARE and treatment of the mentally ill and the evaluation of the mental health movement have been well described and documented elsewhere (Brand, 1968; Cowen and Zax, 1967; Deutsch, 1948; Ridenour, 1961). This chapter will outline some of the major trends and highlights in mental health that are most relevant to education, training, and "manpower production"; manpower growth will be traced primarily through the development of the four major mental health disciplines—psychiatry, psychology, psychiatric social work, and psychiatric nursing. The growth of the mental health movement, particularly post-World War II, has been intimately linked with the development of these four disciplines. From the standpoint of professional manpower, they are the predominant groups, but it is certainly not implied that they are the only ones.

Although informed and interested citizens and citizens' groups were responsible for major changes in care and treatment over the years, mental illness and health received comparatively little national attention until the close of World War II. By the time the war had ended in 1945, most people had become aware that approximately 1,100,000 men had been rejected for military duty because of mental or neurological conditions, and that some 40 per cent of inductees who subsequently received medical discharges had psychiatric disorders. Public awareness was also directed to the apparent effectiveness during the war of early and intensive psychiatric intervention and care.

The magnitude and cost of psychiatric illness and disability were further examined in a series of articles, exposés, and books, such as those of Albert Deutsch (1948), which revealed the deplorable state of affairs that existed in American mental institutions. Thus, in a very constricted period of time, public concern was aroused, heightened, and focused on mental illness.

At the same time the Veterans Administration (VA) was confronted with the continued care and treatment of the thousands of ex-servicemen who required psychiatric treatment and hospitalization following military service. As a result, the shortage and unavailability of professionally trained personnel to deal with the full scope of the needs became evident.

At the start of World War II, there were some 3,000 psychiatrists in the entire country, and for all practical purposes these were the only trained personnel available to deal with serious mental disorders. Under the pressures of military needs, physicians, psychologists, social workers, etc., were pressed into psychiatric service and functions with no prior training or experience or professional involvement. The task facing the VA at the close of the war was an overwhelming one requiring immediate action to develop increased numbers of professionals trained to deal with psychiatric problems. As a result, training programs, involving the cooperating universities and medical schools in the country, were established to expand and develop manpower in psychiatry and clinical psychology.

In 1946, the total national mental health situation, including the public's awareness of need, provided the impetus for passage of the National Mental Health Act (P.L. 79–487), which authorized the U.S. Public Health Service to provide financial assistance and leadership for research on the causes of mental disorders, the training of professional personnel, and assistance to the states for the establishment of clinics, hospitals, and treatment centers for the diagnosis, prevention, and treatment of mental disorders. This legislation has come to be viewed as the most important single development in the history of the mental health movement (Romano, 1967). Based upon this legislation, the National Institute of Mental Health (NIMH) was formally established in 1949, and has developed into the major federal instrumentality for far-ranging and extensive programs in the areas of mental illness and health.

The establishment of the training programs of the VA, the passage of the National Mental Health Act, and the establishing of the NIMH were major national milestones in and of themselves, but they were merely the beginning of a new era in federal responsibility for the health of the American citizen, a responsibility that continues to grow and expand up to this time.

In 1955, Congress passed the Mental Health Study Act (P.L. 84–182), which directed the establishment of a Joint Commission on Mental Illness and Health, whose purpose was to "analyze and evaluate the needs and resources of the mentally ill in the United States and to make recommendations for a national mental health program" (Joint Commission, 1961, p. vii). The report of the Joint Commission was concluded in 1961 and presented a series of recommendations that detailed the major components of a national mental health program, which had major implications for, and made increased demands upon, manpower resources (Joint Commission, 1961). Part of the total study of the commission was a detailed study of mental health manpower, the conclusions and predictions of which were rather gloomy:

Sufficient professional personnel to eliminate the glaring deficiencies in our care of mental patients will never become available if the present population trend continues without commensurate increase in the recruitment and training of mental health manpower. The only possibilities for changing this negative outlook for hundreds of thousands of mental hospital patients would require a great change in our social attitudes, and a consequent massive national effort in all areas of education, including large increases in the number of persons engaged in mental health work, or a sharp break-through in mental health research (Ewalt, 1959, p. ix).

Since the inception of the mental health programs, one of the most critical problems facing the mental health field has been, and remains, the lack of trained manpower to provide care and treatment, to train new persons, and to conduct the research that offers the hope of more adequate solutions to these problems. The magnitude of the task can be evaluated by consideration of the basic data in Table 1, which give estimates of professional mental health manpower available in 1950 and in 1966. The considerable growth demonstrated has to be considered against a background of unprecedented population growth rising from over 152 million in 1950 to over 200 million in 1967. This growth trend is expected to continue, with projections given of over 228 million by 1975 and over 361 million by the year 2000 (U.S. Census, 1967). Enumeration per se has, of course, limited utility and presents only a partial picture of the total situation. Our society has changed drastically in the last two decades; the increased demand and expectation for services in all segments of health, education, and welfare have been phenomenal, and the competition for educated and trained persons grows more acute.

Table 1. Estimated Growth in Numbers of Professionals
in Mental Health, 1950–66

Discipline	1950[a]	1966
Psychiatrists	5,500	19,532[b]
Psychologists	3,500	18,430[c]
Social workers	3,000	12,100[d]
Nurses	10,000	26,800[e]
Total	22,000	75,650

[a] NIMH estimates of professionals involved in mental health activities.
[b] Includes nonpsychiatrically trained physicians who reported primary specialization in psychiatry (Lockman, 1966; NIMH, 1967, p. 23, Table 8).
[c] Includes M.A. and Ph.D. psychologists engaged in mental health–related work activity (NIMH, 1966; National Science Foundation, 1966; American Psychological Association, unpublished data, membership statistics).
[d] Based on number of social workers employed in psychiatric settings (HEW, 1966).
[e] Based on report of "present area of clinical practice" (psychiatric and/or mental health nursing) (American Nurses' Association, unpublished data, national census of employed registered nurses).

Within the mental health field itself, new and changing concepts of treatment, research, and teaching all point to the need for increasing numbers of trained manpower as the vehicle for their implementation.

In 1945, at the beginning of the new national awareness of the need for action, the baseline for this manpower pool was so low that massive efforts were needed for expansion. The steps undertaken to date have resulted in marked development in the mental health professions. Development and expansion of this manpower pool required vast increases in funding over the minimal level that had been previously devoted to mental health training. Table 2 shows the continued, progressive growth in the appropriations for the NIMH over the years, including the growth in monies for the development of manpower and training programs. National expenditures for mental illness and health on all levels, i.e., federal, state, and local, have also continued to grow steadily over the years, concomitant with the realization of the extent and magnitude of the issues involved. A recent estimate of the cost to the nation of mental illness (direct expenditures plus productivity losses, etc.), released by the director of the NIMH, conservatively places the figure at $20 billion a year (Conley, Conwell, and Arrill, 1967).

In 1956, congressional authorization was given to the NIMH for the awarding of Special Mental Health Project Grants (P.L. 84–911) for the development of improved methods of care, treatment, and rehabilitation of the mentally ill. These projects laid the groundwork for community care approaches, a concept ultimately embodied in the Community Mental Health Centers Act of 1963 (P.L. 88–164), which

Table 2. *Total NIMH Appropriations and Funds for Training,*
Fiscal Years 1948–67[a]

(IN MILLIONS)

Fiscal year	NIMH appropriations	NIMH funds for training	Fiscal year	NIMH appropriations	NIMH funds for training
1948	$ 6.4	$ 1.1	1958	$ 39.2	$14.5
1949	9.1	1.6	1959	52.4	19.6
1950	11.6	3.1	1960	68.1	22.9
1951	9.5	3.6	1961	100.9	28.4
1952	10.6	4.2	1962	108.9	39.0
1953	10.9	4.1	1963	143.6	49.3
1954	12.1	4.4	1964	183.3	65.5
1955	14.1	4.6	1965	187.9	75.5
1956	18.0	6.2	1966	232.7	86.2
1957	35.2	11.9	1967	264.1	95.6

[a] NIMH, unpublished data.

provides funds for construction of such centers and specifies the types of services that must be provided in order to qualify for such assistance. Recognizing the need to provide staffing for such centers, Congress passed additional legislation in 1965 that authorized funds to assist in staffing the centers (P.L. 89–1051).

During the early 1950's, the states were also beginning to attempt to improve their mental health offerings on their own, and a series of community mental health acts was passed in a number of state legislatures to permit state funds to be provided to local communities for the construction of community treatment facilities. The first such legislation was passed by New York State in 1954 with other states following.

The foregoing discussion has attempted, in a most truncated fashion, an over-all description of the major events and trends leading to the development of the mental health field as it is today. Emphasis has been given to national legislation and actions that provided both the impetus and the funds for the rapid and continuous expansion of mental health manpower, services, and facilities.

Traditionally, as previously mentioned, the fields of psychiatry, clinical psychology, psychiatric social work, and psychiatric nursing have been looked upon as the "core disciplines" in the mental health field. Consequently, a more detailed look at some of the developmental highlights of each of these separate groups will serve as a meaningful vehicle for further understanding of the growth of the entire mental health field. The more detailed understanding of the individual professions is also necessary background for the conceptual issues and problems that are integral to the basic manpower equation of need, supply, and demand.

PSYCHIATRY

Since psychiatry is the medical specialty dealing with the care and treatment of mental disorders, a complete history of psychiatry would, of necessity, have to deal with the changes and developments in American medicine for a full understanding of its growth and development, not only in relation to the fields of mental health, but also as a function of the changing medical scene. Although American psychiatry has a long history, beginning with the founding of the American Psychiatric Association (APA) in 1844 by a group of superintendents of public mental institutions, its relation to other medical specialties has not always been close, stemming primarily from the attitudes and beliefs regarding mental illness and the isolation of the mental patient in state hospitals. Although the humane and "moral treatment" of institutionalized mental patients, as exemplified by Pinel in France and Tuke in England, had its counterpart here in the efforts of individuals such as Woodward at the Worcester State Hospital in the early nineteenth century, a variety of social and individual circumstances resulted in regression of initially therapeutic institutions toward merely custodial care (Brand, 1968; Grob, 1966).

In the first twenty years of this century, membership in the APA was broadened as the influence of the European psychiatrists began to be felt (Albee, 1959; Brand, 1968). A number of those influenced by Freud, such as Brill, White, and Jeliffe, became leaders on the American scene. Others formulated their concepts on somewhat different bases—Meyer and his concept of psychobiology; Salmon, Bond, and Strecker with their interest in psychological and sociological factors (Appel and Morris, 1963). World War I influenced a trend toward concern with the less severe emotional disorders, as a result of the all too frequently observed "shell-shocked" soldiers suffering from what would today be called traumatic neuroses. Later developments, such as the establishment of clinics, increased interest in and application of psychoanalysis, development of the fields of psychobiology, psychosomatic medicine, neurology, and child psychiatry, all had the effect of beginning to move the locus of functioning of psychiatrists out of the mental hospital (Albee, 1959). The 1930's saw the advent of the shock therapies, another major importation from the European scene, which offered considerable hope for treatment of the functional psychoses.

In the last several decades, psychiatry has undergone major changes in its concepts and methods as its focus has changed from the study and treatment of abnormal behavior to the wider conceptual base of mental health. These changes reflect increased awareness of the importance of the total ecology in the understanding of man, as well as the increased scientific inputs from an ever-increasing range of fields. Gradually, psychiatrists have become aware that "abnormal behavior cannot be properly understood unless the conditions that govern those who do not become ill are also known" (Group for the Advancement of Psychiatry (GAP), 1964, p. 335). Consequently, concepts of training and curricula have changed to incorporate knowledge of the sociologic, ecologic, psychologic, and biologic aspects of human behavior. The changing conceptual base has resulted in changed treatment approaches to emotional disorder. The development of the psychotropic drugs has, in addition, made it possible to modify the behavior of previously unmanageable or unreachable patients so that they become more accessible to psychological modes of treatment.

We have seen the favorable impact of milieu therapy and group therapy, the introduction of new drugs that relieve distressing mental symptoms, and advances in genetics, biochemistry, and physiology that are directly relevant for psychiatry. It has become increasingly possible to treat mentally ill patients in the community (Barton and Malamud, 1964, p. viii).

Over the years, as previously mentioned, the primary treatment locus for the psychiatrist has changed and expanded to include not only the hospital (where the average patient's length of stay has been drastically reduced) but also the community and a variety of outpatient facilities, all resulting in increased demands for direct services and psychiatric consultation. The development of social psychiatry and the community mental health centers approach to mental illness and health is the culmination of the increased incorporation into psychiatry of the broadened conceptual base mentioned earlier and the emphasis upon early treatment and prophylaxis.

The increased acceptance of the social and psychological components of human functioning in the society at large has had its counterpart in the entire medical profession despite earlier reluctance to incorporate such ideas into medical practice. As a result, the demands for psychiatric consultation from the body of medicine itself have grown tremendously, placing even further demands on a rather limited manpower pool (GAP, 1962). The extent of the acceptance of these ideas and their ramifications can be judged by the findings of studies of practicing physicians who estimate from 30 per cent to 60 per cent of their patients to be suffering from some form of psychological disturbance; another study reports 47 per cent of the patients studied to have psychophysiological illnesses as a basis for their complaints (GAP, 1964).

Formal psychiatric education as part of general medical education is of only recent origin. This is of particular significance, not only in view of the large numbers of nonhospitalized mentally ill, but in terms of the psychologic aspects of medical practice mentioned above. The famous Flexner report of 1910 barely mentioned psychiatric teaching, and in 1912 the total teaching requirement for psychiatry, as stipulated by the American Association of Medical Colleges, was twenty hours. By 1914, a survey indicated, the average total time devoted to teaching psychiatry was between thirty and forty hours (of a total of 4,000 hours in four years of medical education). A recent study of the teaching of psychiatry and behavioral science in schools of medicine (Webster, 1967) now shows an average of 362 curriculum hours in the typical school. Six of the 86 medical schools in 1914 offered only an introduction to psychiatry ("medical psychology") during the preclinical years, and five taught no psychiatry. Growth in this area was slow for the next twenty years, and the training of this period emphasized the collection of detailed anamnestic data and writing of personal biographies typical of the psychobiologic approach (GAP, 1962, pp. 9–10).

A study of trends over an eight-year period, beginning in 1932, of preclinical and clinical instruction and residency training showed growth in numbers of hours of psychiatric instruction and in numbers of schools offering it. Of the series of recommendations made on extension of training, most have been put into effect (GAP, 1962, pp. 10–12).

Since 1940, a number of other significant reports have appeared that have influenced medical education. A 1948 report of the Group for the Advancement of Psychiatry formulated the function of psychiatry in medical education and advocated the teaching of psychiatry throughout the medical course, not as a specialty, but as an integral part of medical sciences and practice (GAP, 1948). A second was a report on a 1951 conference held at Ithaca, New York (APA, 1952), which considered objectives, content, and methods of teaching psychiatry in medical schools; it was urged that the basic aim of undergraduate psychiatric teaching be to equip the student with a reasonably adequate knowledge of the facts of human nature; the clinical aim is to familiarize him, through representative clinical experience, with the common and most important problems of patients as persons, and to cultivate at least rudimentary skill and judgment in managing the doctor-patient relationship. The Ithaca study found data indicating diversified patterns of teaching practices, with growing numbers of medical schools teaching psychiatry in all four years and much psychiatric teaching being integrated with that of other departments.

As an outgrowth of the Ithaca conference, an outline for a curriculum for teaching psychiatry was prepared in 1956 by the Committee on Medical Education of the APA. This suggested the teaching of personality growth and development, psychopathology, interviewing techniques, and the therapeutic use of interpersonal relationships in medicine (GAP, 1962).

The GAP report on the preclinical teaching of psychiatry characterized the 1930's as an era of psychobiologic and psychosomatic expansion, the 1940's as a period of psychodynamic and psychoanalytic expansion, and the 1950's as the introductory period of the social and behavioral sciences.

It discussed at length the continuing growth in the 1960's of the role of the behavioral sciences in medical education (GAP, 1962). A recent meeting, jointly sponsored by the APA and the Association of American Medical Colleges (Conference on Psychiatry and Medical Education, Atlanta, June, 1967), addressed itself to the reevaluation and revision of the medical school psychiatric curriculum in keeping with the changes and developments of the past decade.

The residency aspect of training was the subject of a 1952 Ithaca conference (APA, 1953). Residency training was inaugurated at Johns Hopkins in 1889 for men who had completed their internships, and superceded the older method of having new physicians "in residency" for general practical experience. As developed at Johns Hopkins, residency was closely supervised with training in basic sciences as well as in practical techniques in the particular specialty. Although opportunities for residencies of all types had grown from 2,000 in 1930 to almost 19,000 in 1950,[1] psychiatry was a relative latecomer in this respect, and has provided increasing numbers of opportunities only since the early 1930's.

The American Board of Psychiatry and Neurology was established in 1934. In order to be certified, residents must be trained for three years at institutions that meet standards regarding types of patients seen, basic sciences provided, type of supervision, collaborative work with other disciplines, and training in neurology as prescribed by the Council on Medical Education of the American Medical Association. An examination is given that now includes written, oral, and practical components.

The psychiatric manpower pool as it stands today is composed of many persons with educational backgrounds far different from the pattern described above for three-year residency training as preparation for ultimate board certification. A 1965 study conducted jointly by the NIMH and the APA revealed 18,750 psychiatrists in the United States. Of those for whom information on length of residency was available, 71 per cent had three or more years of residency training, 9 per cent had two years, 10 per cent had one year or less, and 10 per cent had none. More than one third of the respondents (37 per cent) were certified by the American Board of Psychiatry and Neurology (Lockman, 1966). Thus, it is possible for a physician with less than three years of residency training to limit his practice to psychiatry and identify himself as a psychiatrist.

The growth of the field of psychiatry from the post-World War II period to the present is shown in Table 3. Information on the types of activities undertaken by psychiatrists is essential as a basis for understanding the utilization of their time and the nature of total psychiatric practice. Table 4, from the joint NIMH-APA study (Lockman, 1966), presents the percentages of time spent in various activities by the study sample. While psychiatry is still to a great extent private-practice-oriented, a

1. For 1966–67, total residencies offered for all medical specialties was 39,384.

*Table 3. Psychiatry Training Programs, Estimated Number of Psychiatrists,
and Ratios of Psychiatrists to Population: 1945–66* [a]

| | APPROVED TRAINING PROGRAMS: GENERAL PSYCHIATRY | | | ESTIMATED NUMBER OF PSYCHIATRISTS | |
| | | RESIDENCIES OFFERED | | | |
Year	*No.*	*No.*	*% filled*	*Total* [b]	*Per 100,000 pop.* [c]
1945	143	742	N.A.	3,634	2.6
1946	159	885	N.A.	4,010	2.8
1947	241	1,470	N.A.	4,341	3.0
1948	227	1,618	N.A.	4,678	3.2
1949	231	1,754	80	6,686	4.5
1950	232	1,768	70	7,090	4.7
1951	246	1,936	71	7,851	5.1
1952	247	2,456	73	8,909	5.7
1953	260	2,335	70	9,240	5.8
1954	265	2,506	72	10,147	6.2
1955	279	2,696	72	10,623	6.4
1956	274	2,968	73	11,413	6.8
1957	281	3,308	76	12,312	7.2
1958	288	3,542	78	13,190	7.5
1959	303	3,658	82	14,046	7.9
1960	308	3,737	83	14,823	8.2
1961	321	4,026	80	15,695	8.5
1962	338	4,231	77	16,360	8.8
1963	339	4,291	76	17,013	9.0
1964	287	4,429	78	17,657	9.2
1965	265	4,495	79	18,750	9.7
1966	258	4,493	79	19,532	10.0

APPROVED TRAINING PROGRAMS: CHILD PSYCHIATRY

| | | RESIDENCIES OFFERED | |
Year	*No.*	*No.*	*% filled*
1960	58	101	78
1961	76	255	79
1962	96	330	74
1963	117	450	76
1964	103	486	72
1965	100	505	66
1966	111	553	68

[a] Data from: AMA, 1967; APA, 1967; Lockman, 1966; U.S. Census, 1966.

[b] Estimate is obtained from APA membership figures and total number of residencies filled in both psychiatry and child psychiatry. Membership figures are for either March or May of the year shown. The 1965 figure is the result of a survey conducted by the APA of the nation's psychiatrists.

[c] Based on population estimates as of July 1 of the year shown for the total population, including Alaska, Hawaii, and armed forces abroad.

Table 4. *Distribution of Respondent Psychiatrists by Remunerated Hours Worked per Week and by Professional Activity: 1965* [a]

| REMUNERATED HOURS PER WEEK | PROFESSIONAL WORK ACTIVITY | | | | | | | | | | | | |
| | DIRECT SERVICES | | CONSULTATION | | TEACHING | | RESEARCH | | ADMINIS-TRATION | | AS TRAINEE | | TOTAL HOURS | |
	No.	%	No.	%	No.	%	No.	%	No.	%	No.	%	No.	%
None	2,095	14.7	7,792	54.7	9,025	63.3	12,056	84.6	9,734	68.3	12,460	87.4	—	—
1 – 14	1,402	9.8	5,621	39.4	4,485	31.5	1,691	11.9	2,818	19.8	436	3.1	194	1.3
15 – 29	2,766	19.4	546	3.8	632	4.4	296	2.1	928	6.5	279	2.0	560	3.8
30 – 34	1,417	9.9	83	0.6	56	0.4	62	0.4	160	1.1	37	0.2	533	3.6
35 – 44	3,972	27.9	127	0.9	42	0.3	121	0.8	520	3.6	578	4.1	6,335	43.2
45 & up	2,596	18.2	79	0.6	8	0.1	22	0.2	88	0.6	458	3.2	7,030	48.0
Total answering	14,248	100.0	14,248	100.0	14,248	100.0	14,248	100.0	14,248	100.0	14,248	100.0	14,652	100.0

[a] Lockman, 1966, p. 9, Table 4.

considerable proportion of practitioners engages in secondary, public service activities. A recent NIMH survey (Arnhoff and Shriver, 1966) details the current professional characteristics of a large group of psychiatrists who at some time in their professional training received stipends under the training-grant program of the NIMH. The data show the type of organizations in which those primarily in private practice spend the second largest segment of their time (Table 5).

Although the growth in the profession has been considerable since 1945, psychiatry is well aware of the impossibility of any drastic increase in output to match current conceptions of need. While it has been possible over the years to increase the percentage of medical school graduates who choose psychiatry as a specialty, it is questionable how much elasticity remains in this direction. Since psychiatry draws upon M.D.s for its residents, its manpower pool is a direct function of the broader problems of medical education and the physician shortage (Fein, 1967).

The 1960's have seen a marked increase in awareness of the need for preventive efforts in contrast to the direct individual-treatment emphasis of the past; traditional medical approaches to disease control, as exemplified by classical epidemiology and public health medicine, have increasingly been utilized. Consequently, psychiatric involvement and consultation in social and community processes have markedly increased, with the dual concerns of increasing the effectiveness of a finite number of trained professionals and of changing the processes and conditions that engender psychological disturbance and malfunction. The importance of the growth and developmental process was reflected in the establishment in 1960 of the formally recognized specialty of child psy-

---

Table 5. *Type of Employing Organization in which Second Highest Amount of Time Is Spent for Those Former Trainees in Psychiatry Primarily in Private Practice*[a]

Type of organization	% of group
Medical school	17
Academic institution (other)	4
Industry or business	1
Education, health, or welfare agency	4
Courts and correctional institutions	1
Elementary or secondary school system	2
Hospitals/clinics	49
Research organization or laboratory	2
Other	3
None	17
Total %	100

[a]Arnhoff and Shriver, 1966, p. 24, Table 24.

chiatry. The growth and development of the areas of social psychiatry and community psychiatry, via the community mental health movement, are reflective of this increased psychiatric participation in social community process.

Although the desirability of prevention of disturbance, as exemplified by public health medicine, logically follows from the history of medical success via this approach, it is not without its conceptual problems when applied to human behavior in a social community context. The issues posed by these developments have been detailed by psychiatric writers as well as others (Albee, 1967a, 1967b; Gruenberg, 1967; Leighton, 1967; Redlich, 1967; Szasz, 1961; Turner and Cumming, 1967), and resolution has not yet been found. Since these conceptual issues are basic not only to those of psychiatric manpower and its utilization but also to those of mental illness and mental health in general, they will be discussed and amplified throughout the following chapters.

PSYCHOLOGY

From its formal beginning, psychology has been an academically oriented research field, a heritage that continues to the present time. Because of this, however, psychology's involvement in mental illness and health prior to World War II was primarily one of research, centering on issues of measurement of mental functions, abilities, and individual differences. This has been a traditional interest and activity of psychologists and provided the skill and manpower for test construction, development, and screening in World War I (the Army Alpha test). Following World War I, the psychologist's role as a specialist in psychological tests and measurements was well established. With the development of the child welfare stations, psychologists combined the expertise in testing with interest in child psychology and development, continuing research in individual differences and mental measurement. The primary orientation of the field, however, continued to be that of academic science, although some effort was directed toward problems of education and child guidance. There was as yet no definable specialty of clinical psychology, nor had a firm professional role emerged (Rubinstein and Lorr, 1954); historically, however, it is interesting to note that the term "clinical psychology" was used by Witmer in 1896 and that professional concerns were voiced by Cattell in 1904 (Watson, 1953).

As a consequence of World War II, in which the mental health needs were found to far outstrip manpower availability, a large number of psychologists were introduced to a wide range of applied areas of professional and scientific application while in the armed forces. In addition to their traditional roles in scientific research and psychological test construction, they became more active in psychodiagnosis and played a major role in neuropsychiatric screening. Among the applications of psychology that were introduced to psychologists was that of psychotherapy in all its forms. Thus another dimension was added to the psychologist's role model of research tester—that of psychotherapist (Tyler and Speisman, 1967).

In 1946, the American Psychological Association was requested by the NIMH and the VA to undertake evaluation and accreditation of universities for doctoral training in clinical psychology, and to provide a guide for all federal agencies involved in training activities. The American Psychological Association established an Education and Training Board to accomplish these tasks, and the first steps were undertaken to rapidly develop and expand the professional as well as the scientific components of psychology (Peck and Ash, 1964).

The Division of Clinical Psychology of the American Psychological Association was formed, and for the first time the completion of a supervised clinical internship in addition to the Ph.D. was required for division membership.

Another major step in role and functional definition had now been taken by psychology: the formal beginnings of a professional role as distinct from, yet in addition to, its primarily research and scientific activities of the past. Concomitant with the expansion of professional role and functioning, concern for professional standards and criteria emerged. The American Board of Examiners in Professional Psychology (ABEPP) was established in 1947 in the areas of clinical, counseling, and industrial psychology. In much the same manner as the medical specialty boards, this body was established to serve as an examining and certifying body for professional competence and experience. In addition, many individual states, at the instigation of state psychological associations, have since passed licensing or certification laws for psychologists to establish standards of professional competence to protect the public interest.

From this postwar period of time to the present, the growth in the entire field of psychology has been considerable. The membership in the American Psychological Association, the best single index of the number of psychologists in the country, has risen from 4,173 in 1945 to 25,800 in 1967; the number of graduate departments of psychology granting the Ph.D. has grown from 37 in 1948 to 105 in 1966; and the annual production of Ph.D.'s has increased from 154 in 1948 to 1,133 in 1966 (Table 6).

While clinical psychology remains the segment of the total field most closely and traditionally identified with mental illness and health, the delineation is not as clear as it is in psychiatry or psychiatric nursing. Not only is this a function of the continued definitional problem as to what precisely is mental health, it also relates to the far-ranging conceptual involvements in human behavior that are directly relevant to psychology and, therefore, to mental health. This is emphasized by the recent analyses of the 1964 and 1966 National Science Foundation (NSF) Register of

Table 6. Growth in Graduate Departments of Psychology, Annual Production of M.A. and Ph.D. Psychologists, and Membership in the American Psychological Association: 1945–67 [a]

YEAR	GRADUATE DEPARTMENTS AWARDING EACH DEGREE		M.A.'S AWARDED IN PSYCHOLOGY	PH.D.'S AWARDED IN PSYCHOLOGY[b]	MEMBERSHIP IN APA
	Master's	Doctor's			
1945	N.A.	N.A.	N.A.	N.A.	4,173
1946	N.A.	N.A.	N.A.	N.A.	4,427
1947	N.A.	N.A.	N.A.	N.A.	4,661
1948	109	37	1,200	154	5,754
1949	113	38	1,455	201	6,735
1950	137	44	1,316	283	7,273
1951	144	51	1,645	425	8,554
1952	140	57	1,406	540	9,512
1953	141	63	1,161	583	10,903
1954	156	66	1,254	619	12,380
1955	160	69	1,293	688	13,475
1956	152	73	973	634	14,509
1957	152	73	1,095	550	15,545
1958	162	74	1,235	745	16,644
1959	167	75	1,257	787	17,448
1960	175	80	1,406	773	18,215
1961	173	79	1,719	820	18,948
1962	194	87	1,832	857	19,947
1963	189	95	1,918	892	20,989
1964	186	94	2,059	1,013	22,119
1965	199	101	2,241	955	23,561
1966	212	105	2,530	1,133	24,473
1967	N.A.	N.A.	N.A.	N.A.	25,800

[a] Data from: APA unpublished data; NAS, 1967, pp. 7–8, Table 1; OE, unpublished data.

[b] These figures understate the number of degrees in psychology, because those awarded through departments of education are not included.

Scientific and Technical Personnel, in which 61 per cent of the psychologists responding, representing all areas of psychology, considered their work to be relevant to mental health, broadly defined (Compton, 1966; NIMH, 1966; NSF, 1965; NSF, 1966).

As might be expected, the change from a purely academic scientific field to one incorporating major professional components has caused drastic and continued soul-searching on the part of the science profession as to the nature of its role, curriculum requirements, etc. The research-based scientific orientation for any psychologist has remained and is fundamental to the training of all psychologists, regardless of specialization. Psychology continues to be, of all the mental health professions, the most active in mental health research: the overwhelming majority of mental health research is conducted by psychologists, and a recent survey of psychologists revealed 79 per cent involved in research (Arnhoff and Shriver, 1966).

The model of the research-trained clinician, the professional who is also a scientist, was first outlined in the 1947 Shakow Report and at the Boulder Conference in 1949 (Raimy, 1950), which was addressed to the problems and issues in the training of psychologists incurred by the field's response to the pressures for their skills and services. These earlier conferences have been followed by several others over the years (Blank, 1964) as part of an ongoing dialogue to relate education, training, and practice to the conditions imposed by a rapidly changing society with intense demands for trained manpower. Although society, mental health practice, and psychology itself have changed over the years, the scientific base for professional practice has remained as the *sine qua non* for psychological training and professional practice.

While the science and the profession are well aware of the need to develop more psychological manpower, especially in the service realm, the issue of less than doctoral training remains unresolved and controversial, and the primary model is that of the doctorally trained person. The suggestion that subdoctoral programs be developed, experimented with, and systematically examined has been made at most of the conferences devoted to graduate training up to the present (Blank, 1964). Questions as to quality control, curriculum, and tasks and functions to be performed by such trained persons continue to be debated. Approximately 2,500 master's degrees in psychology are now awarded annually, but many of their recipients continue on to the doctorate. A 1963 NIMH survey of mental health establishments found that 46.9 per cent of the psychologists so employed had less than the doctoral degree (NIMH, 1965a). Approximately 3,500–4,000 new students enter graduate training in psychology each year; there is no shortage of qualified applicants, with a typical department admitting 10 per cent–20 per cent of its applicants (Brayfield, 1967).

From data obtained from NIMH follow-up surveys of its former trainees (Arnhoff and Shriver, 1966) and from the American Psychological Association (Brayfield, 1967), it is clear that psychology as a whole is a public service profession with the majority employed in public or nonprofit settings. Of those identified as "mental health" psychologists, the APA reports over 90 per cent employed in public or nonprofit settings. Only 7 per cent of all psychologists are self-employed and another 8 per cent are in private industry.

Ever since the formal inception and development of the field of clinical psychology in 1946, the primary locus of work for clinical psychologists has been in mental hospitals and psychiatric clinics. This is a reflection of the initial training programs developed in VA hospitals and state mental hospitals, as well as of the initial dependency upon the field of psychiatry, which provided the role models and orientation for the neophyte profession. By the mid-1950's, attention began to focus on broader conceptions of mental health and illness and on human social functioning in general. Specifically, approaches to the nation's vast mental health problems began to be viewed in a nonmedical context with emphasis given to mental health outside of the hospital and clinic and focusing on preventive approaches to behavior disorder and maximization of human potential and effectiveness.

At the 1955 Stanford Conference on Psychology and Mental Health (Strother, 1956), Dr. Robert Felix, then director of the NIMH, gave an address in which he urged psychologists to explore and develop nonmedical approaches and contributions to the nation's mental health problems, specifically emphasizing the social process in the community. Such an orientation, however, posed additional changes in self-perception and role development in a young field still searching for its own identity and concerned with the scientific base for therapeutic interventions. Innovations in training programs, however, began to emerge, and along with the concurrent broadening of the concepts of mental health, the work locus of clinical psychologists began to change to include settings other than the hospital and clinic.

In speaking of mental health and mental illness in a traditional sense, the specialty of clinical psychology has been most directly involved. By 1956, however, it had become obvious that more of all types of psychologists were needed, both to train clinical psychologists and to engage in research, and that psychology as a behavioral science was generic to all mental health efforts. Awareness of the behavioral base and its relevance to an increasing range of social functioning has continued to grow. Increased demands are being made upon contributions from psychologists, not only for direct service, but for research assistance to other fields and the teaching of nonpsychologists. Thus, a recent analysis of psychologists in academic settings shows that the majority of academic psychologists are no longer employed in departments of psychology but rather are to be found in schools of medicine, social work, nursing, business administration, etc. (Speisman, 1968), indicating the rapid development, acceptance of, and demands on the field.

National trends of the past few years in the fields of education, social welfare, race relations, and poverty, concomitant with the development of concerns with community mental health, have had tremendous impact on psychology in terms of multiplied stresses not only on existing manpower shortages, but, more importantly, on psychology's conceptual models and reassessed approaches to social functioning. Out of the welter of divergent trends and interests that have occupied professional psychology over the years, the issues and models alluded to above are of particular pertinence to the current mental health scene.

The development of interest in community mental health and the emphasis upon epidemiologic and preventive approaches to human problems, along with a growing research literature, have served to emphasize to psychology the need to explore a broadened approach to the problems of human behavior subsumed by the rubric "mental health." Thus, it has become obvious that the social, developmental, educational, and ecologic activities and interests of psychologists must be brought to bear upon these approaches, and this knowledge combined with the clinical approach. The result has been the development of community psychology (Bennett *et al*; 1966) and the evolution of new training programs to prepare psychologists to function in a broader, more societal fashion than ever before. As a consequence, there has been a tremendous reinvestment of interest in the educational-developmental process (Sarasan, Levine, Goldenberg, Cherlin, and Bennett, 1966) ; school psychology has become one of the most rapidly growing psychological specialties, and interest in the social-personality aspects of behavior also shows enormous growth (Speisman, 1968). While these developments reflect consolidated application of new knowledge and theories, they are also reflective of a new professional maturity of psychology—a developing role model of scientific-professional functioning, which has moved away from "thinking almost exclusively of individuals in distress, and toward developing conceptions of effective functioning, positive mental health, and competence" (Tyler and Speisman, 1967, p. 845) .

While the initial involvement in community psychology came from clinical psychologists, it rapidly became apparent that this was too restrictive an approach and that psychologists of all persuasions were needed. New training models and programs have begun to evolve in their own right and are serving to involve social, educational, child, developmental, and measurement psychologists in far-ranging societal involvement (Cowen, Gardner, and Zax, 1967; Sarasan *et al.*, 1966; Tyler and Speisman, 1967) .

The manpower problems of psychology have been drastically exacerbated by these recent developments within the field itself and by increased societal demand. It has recently been estimated that the entire doctoral output of psychology for the next five years could be absorbed into the teaching faculties of colleges and universities alone (Brayfield, 1967). Projections and estimates made by the NIMH indicate a need for over 2,000 additional professionally trained psychologists for research and services to staff the Community Mental Health Centers by 1970 (H.R., 1965). Since current and anticipated production of psychologists so obviously cannot meet these demands, the search continues for alternative approaches to a solution, focusing primarily on more efficient utilization of manpower.

SOCIAL WORK

Social work has been defined as seeking to "enhance the social functioning of individuals, singly and in groups, by activities focused upon their social relationships which constitute the interaction between man and his environment. These activities can be grouped into three functions: restoration of impaired capacity, provision of individual and social resources, and prevention of social dysfunction" (Boehm, 1959, p. 54).

The first full-time paid welfare workers in this country were probably the employees of the Special Relief Department of the U.S. Sanitary Commission, which was established to aid Union soldiers during the Civil War. This activity ceased after the war, and the next full-time paid workers involved in what would be considered social work appeared on the scene with the development of the Charity Organization Society (COS) movement in the late 1870's and the settlement movement, and the evolution of state and local public welfare programs. The COS agencies, which were found in 92 cities in the United States and Canada by the early 1890's, had as their aim the assistance of the poor through individual services. Even at the beginning, these charity workers had a systematic approach to the problems of poverty. Case records of families served were kept, tasks of the caseworkers, as they ultimately were called, were defined, and coordination was attempted among individuals, groups, and agencies interested in helping. The COS movement was the forerunner of today's family service agency and helped develop family casework, family counseling, schools of social work, employment services, legal aid services, and other aspects of the modern social welfare scene (Kidneigh, 1965).

By 1900, social welfare had become a matter of specialized programs to deal with particular social problems, a characteristic that persists to the present day. There is today a general trend toward social programs that attempt to view individuals and families in the total context of community life (Kidneigh, 1965).

Initially, social workers were trained in proprietary schools that were functional parts of agencies, where teaching, through courses and institutes, focused on agency needs only. Gradually, this process gave way to training courses for the personnel of a series of agencies, where the curriculum reflected the specific problems with which agencies dealt, was descriptive of and focused on situations rather than concepts. Ultimately, independent schools were developed, which eventually affiliated with colleges and universities and achieved closer contact with scientific departments that could contribute to understanding the problems of social work (Boehm, 1959). Table 7 shows the growth in numbers of accredited schools of social work from 1945 through 1967.

The trend, in general, has been one of educating for fundamentals or basic ingredients in order to prepare the student for a variety of tasks, on a variety of levels, and under a variety of auspices. Training for specific areas of practice is expected to occur via staff development in agencies. With the establishment of formalized education in the place of apprenticeships, social work has achieved one of the principal characteristics of a profession. The development of a theoretical base and a theory of practice, though still incomplete (as is true of the other core disciplines), is another qualification for status as a profession (Boehm, 1959).

Social work, like each of the other core disciplines, has, since World War II, been studying itself as a profession, and evaluating and modifying its standards and educational procedures. As of 1963–64, it was estimated to include 125,000 members (U.S. Dept. of Labor, 1964). The social worker is "the indispensable connecting link between the program established by law or other means for meeting problems of social welfare, and the person who is in need of help or benefits through it. . . . New legislation creating or expanding programs of social services has been

Table 7. Growth in Graduate Schools of Social Work. Enrollments, Degrees Awarded, and Membership in Professional Associations: 1945–67 [a]

Academic year	Number of graduate schools of social work [b]	Number enrolled in graduate programs [c]	Number of master's degrees awarded [d]	Membership in NASW [e]	Number of certified social workers [f]
1944–45	42	2,283	839		
1945–46	43	2,603	1,049		
1946–47	44	3,410	1,311		
1947–48	44	3,737	1,765		
1948–49	46	3,716	1,803		
1949–50	48	4,066	1,804		
1950–51	49	4,336	1,923		
1951–52	51	4,195	1,946		
1952–53	53	4,006	1,844		
1953–54	52	3,694	1,651		
1954–55	51	3,512	1,655		
1955–56	52	3,644	1,634		
1956–57	52	3,811	1,612	21,002	
1957–58	53	4,165	1,744	21,799	
1958–59	55	4,551	1,897	22,936	
1959–60	56	4,934	2,087	26,612	
1960–61	56	5,136	2,162	28,214	
1961–62	56	5,496	2,318	34,494	
1962–63	56	6,039	2,505	36,854	21,485
1963–64	58	6,592	2,815	39,554	26,984
1964–65	59	7,366	3,206	42,217	28,822
1965–66	60	8,380	3,693	45,810	28,850
1966–67	63	9,567	4,279	45,850	30,100

[a] Data from: Witte, Kendall, and Hollis, 1955; De Vera, 1967.
[b] Includes only accredited schools in the United States.
[c] Includes fulltime students in both master's and doctoral programs.
[d] Includes only master's degrees.
[e] Membership statistics for the National Association of Social Workers date from January 1, 1956 (NASW, unpublished data, annual report of membership statistics).
[f] Membership statistics for the Academy of Certified Social Workers date from December 31, 1962 (NASW, unpublished data, membership department).

enacted in each session of Congress in recent years, and with it the demand for adequately trained personnel has increased" (HEW, 1965, p. 77).

There are two major types of educational background found among social workers: (1) those with master's degrees from graduate schools of social work whose curriculum requires field work to develop knowledge and competence in practice in any setting; and (2) those with bachelor's degrees and educational preparation in the social and behavioral sciences plus inservice training either in employing agencies or in educational settings geared to providing the specific knowledge and skills appropriate for functioning within the scope of the employing agency.

Until 1959, social work education produced persons trained for special subfields, such as psychiatric social work. In that year a long-standing debate over general versus specific training was finally resolved as a result of a curriculum study of the Council on Social Work Education, which recommended that a common generic base of knowledge applicable to any social problem be provided. This means, with regard to mental health, that any social worker trained under the new approach may be regarded as a potential candidate for employment in a psychiatric setting (Kidneigh, 1965).

Modern social work has drawn upon a variety of the social and behavioral sciences in creating its theory. Developmental psychology, psychoanalytic theory, theories of social organization, the influence of culture on personality—the influence of all these is clearly visible.

Thus one finds social work borrowing ideas from a variety of sources, testing these ideas against the practical situations encountered in working with people, and modifying the contributions accordingly. But social work did not limit itself to borrowing from the social and biological sciences. It also borrowed from other service professions, notably medicine and psychiatry, law and teaching. And to the constellation that emerges from all the borrowing something has been added, evidenced by the increasing stream of social work literature (Kidneigh, 1965, p. 10).

Since 1955, the field has been represented by the National Association of Social Workers (NASW), which resulted from the merger of seven preexisting specialty groups. The growth in its membership is shown in Table 7. In 1960, a certification process was begun and the Academy of Certified Social Workers established. Table 7 also shows data on growth in numbers of certified social workers.

There have been differing opinions as to the definition of psychiatric social work. To some, it has indicated that psychiatric social workers know more psychopathology or are more dynamically oriented than other social workers; to others, psychiatric social workers are those who work with psychiatrists; and to still others, the predominating group, whether or not work is performed in a psychiatric setting has been the key determining factor (Berkman, 1953). For our consideration in evaluating the size of the manpower pool, the problem is a larger one, parallel to that posed in the section on psychology; in view of the definition of social work given earlier, can any social worker be considered to be uninvolved in matters of mental health?

In 1965, the U.S. Department of Health, Education, and Welfare (HEW) published a report of a Departmental Task Force on Social Work Education and Manpower entitled "Closing the Gap in Social Work Manpower," a careful study of the social work manpower situation in health, education, and welfare agencies and the causes of and solutions to the problems. The report presented figures compiled from data from the Bureau of Labor Statistics and the NASW indicating that there were in 1950, 2,253 psychiatric social workers, of whom 1,456 had graduate education. In 1960, the number had risen to 5,171, of whom 3,717 had graduate training. By 1964, there were 7,359 psychiatric social workers with graduate training, double the 1960 figure (HEW, 1965). The NIMH estimate of social workers with the M.S. in social work with mental health relevant training in 1967 is 13,676 (NIMH, 1967).

Of all the disciplines supported for mental health relevant training by the NIMH, social work has had support for the largest number of individuals, over 10,000 since 1947 (NIMH, unpublished data).

According to a recent NIMH survey (1965b), an estimated 7,500 social workers were employed in approximately 2,500 mental health establishments in early 1963. Roughly 75 per cent of the social workers surveyed reported a master's degree, 13 per cent some graduate training, and another 1 per cent a doctorate (Table 8).

"Closing the Gap in Social Work Manpower" concludes that as far as the mental health field is concerned, in addition to a better geographic distribution of social workers, there must be a

substantial increase in the ratio of personnel with professional education to total social work staff, and a stepping up of the rate of social work personnel available in relation to the number of persons in the population to be served (HEW, 1965, p. 19).

The overall extreme continuing need, despite the rate of growth of the field, is reinforced by data from the VA, which is the largest single employer of social workers with graduate social work education in the United States. VA Social Work Service has grown from 109 in 1944 to 1,687 in 1964, yet they report that the demand for social services has consistently outrun the increase in the staff available.

The conclusion is unavoidable . . . that the health field is seriously undermanned in social work personnel, that geographic coverage is most uneven, and the rate of growth in demand is so rapid that there is an ever-widening gap between needed and available manpower for services . . . (HEW, 1965, p. 21).

Table 8. Social Work Staffing Patterns of Mental Health Establishments by Highest Level of Education[a]

TYPE OF ESTABLISHMENT	TOTAL[b]		GRADUATE DEGREE			LESS THAN MASTER'S DEGREE
	No.	%	Total	Doctorate	Master's	
Outpatient clinic	4,128	100.0	85.1	1.3	83.8	14.9
Public hospitals	2,737	100.0	64.0	0.2	63.8	36.0
Private hospitals	144	100.0	86.7	0.7	86.0	13.3
Public institutions for the mentally retarded	523	100.0	51.1	0.8	50.3	48.9
Private institutions for the mentally retarded	58	100.0	69.0	—	69.0	31.0
Total	7,259	100.0	75.2	0.8	74.4	24.4[c]

[a] Adapted from: Eldridge, 1965b, p. xi, Table A–9; NIMH, 1965b, p. 2, Table 1.

[b] A person employed in more than one establishment was counted in each place where he was employed, thus producing multiple entries. The figure 7,259 is the total number of social workers responding to the survey. It includes 29 respondents who did not specify highest educational level.

[c] Of the total 7,259 social workers responding, 13.4 per cent had some graduate study but no graduate degree and 11.0 per cent had a bachelor's degree or less.

The competition for such persons in the entire health field, therefore, becomes ever more acute as the nation's total health and social welfare programs increase, and the mental health field competes with the total field for its needed share.

The relevant issues in the study of critical manpower needs have recently been highlighted by French (1964). While he wrote specifically in the context of social work manpower, the relevance of the issues to all of the mental health professions is obvious. He points out that the source of demand for social welfare personnel stems from the dislocations resulting from technological advances in our society. This requires that those responsible for staffing welfare services understand the pace, direction, and consequences of the second industrial revolution. In addition, the social welfare institutions are themselves changing, leading to changes in the types and numbers of personnel needed to staff them. Expansion of two-year social work schools will not be sufficient as a solution to shortages, and other solutions will have to be found, such as restructuring positions to enable subprofessional personnel to perform defined functions, or revising the method of dealing with the given social problem. "The task posed to administrators and educators is one of job analysis and creative experimentation with alternative approaches to meeting welfare needs" (French, 1964, p. ii). He also indicates that there is still a critical shortage of persons qualified for leadership roles in social welfare programs: those persons who keep such programs responsive to changing needs.

PSYCHIATRIC NURSING

The history of nursing in this century has evolved around its struggles to establish itself as a profession and to formulate and maintain universal educational standards and curricula. Its two major professional associations had their beginnings in the 1890's. The American Society of Superintendents of Training Schools for Nurses was organized in 1894 and later, in 1912, became the National League of Nursing Education. The latter, with the National Organization for Public Health Nurses and the Association of Collegiate Schools of Nursing, became the National League for Nursing in 1952. The American Nurses' Association, formed in 1911, originated with the formation in 1897 of the Nurses' Associated Alumnae, which began the tremendous effort to secure legal recognition and standardization, state by state.

Initially, training of nurses developed in hospitals more as an exploitative means of obtaining nursing services from the students than from any concern with training itself. They worked long hours in uncomfortable and deprived physical conditions and were required to do a great deal of menial labor. In the history of nursing training, achievement of the distinction between training and nursing service was a major accomplishment (Roberts, 1963).

The origins of the specialty of psychiatric nursing began with the lessened use of physical restraints in the care of institutionalized mental patients in the nineteenth century, which focused attention on the role of the nursing personnel available to care for them.

Freed from restraints, the mentally ill person had to be dealt with as a personality. . . . It thus became necessary to enter with increasing awareness into a psychological relationship with the patient. The progressively expanding concern over the psychological and therapeutic meaning and importance of this relationship constitutes the major development in psychiatric nursing during the last hundred years (Santos and Stainbrook, 1949, p. 50).

The year 1882 is generally cited as the beginning date for the training of nurses in psychiatric facilities in the United States. In that year McLean Hospital in Boston organized a training school for psychiatric nursing under Edward Cowles. It was the first formally organized school of nursing to be established in a mental hospital. Certificates were given to the nurses upon completion of the course; later, in 1886, the hospital affiliated with Massachusetts General Hospital, and nursing students in the field were given credit for a full nursing course upon completion of the senior year at this hospital.

In 1906, standardization of training began with the report of a committee of the American Medico-Psychological Association, which was appointed to "prescribe a minimum course of instruction for training schools for nurses in hospitals for the insane" (Zilboorg and Henry, 1941, p. 589).

The standards established within mental hospital-based training schools, however, were well below those of schools of nursing, so that, ultimately, these were discontinued by the 1930's. Some of the mental hospitals established "postgraduate" courses primarily for the purpose of preparing staff for the institution.

Schools of nursing were quite slow to assume any responsibility for psychiatric nursing training. They began to arrange affiliations with psychiatric hospitals for psychiatric nursing courses in the early 1900's but three decades later only about one half of the nation's schools offered psychiatric nursing in the undergraduate curriculum, and it was not required for state board registration until 1952 (Gregg, 1966). By 1955, all schools in general hospitals provided psychiatric affiliations (Stevens, 1966).

Over the years, three different types of nursing programs developed: (1) the diploma program, which is hospital-based and provides three years of training after high school; (2) the associate-degree program, offered in junior and community colleges, which requires two years of study, including basic science and nursing courses with clinical laboratory offerings in the service units of community hospitals; (3) the baccalaureate program, in colleges and universities, which provides four or five years of training, both academic and clinical. The numbers of each of these types of schools are shown in Table 9.

The first two types of schools prepare technical nursing practitioners, while the third, the collegiate program, prepares the first-level professional-nurse practitioners. The first university school of nursing was established in 1909 at the University of Minnesota. By the beginning of World War II, there were 33 collegiate schools of nursing as defined by the Association of Collegiate Schools of Nursing (Roberts, 1963). These programs were the precursors of today's collegiate education in nursing. Advanced psychiatric nursing education, i.e., training for practice as a clinical nursing specialist, is considered to date from 1943, when the National League of Nursing Education Committee on Postgraduate Clinical Courses began to formulate basic assumptions and guiding principles for advanced courses. Its subcommittee on psychiatric nursing constructed an advanced program of study based upon these principles. In this same period three university schools of nursing established advanced psychiatric nursing programs, and by 1947 four more were in existence (Schmitt, 1949).

Delineation of standards for a national system of accreditation of nursing training programs was an outgrowth of a study by the National League of Nursing Education, supported by the NIMH in the first years of its training-grant program (1948–49). This effort ultimately had a great impact on all of nursing in the country in terms of developing new models and dimensions in nursing education and establishing educational standards. The delineation of standards in psychiatric nursing led all other clinical specialties in nursing to follow suit.

Current thinking in regard to the basic training of nurses is "that all nurses are prepared better for generalized nursing practice in all types of facilities when the nursing education is offered in a collegiate institution and when general and professional education are included in the curriculum," and a major theme is "that the needs of all patients would be served better by including psychiatric nursing as an important aspect in the education of all nurses" (Peplau, 1958, p. 37). Thus, as is the case in social work and medical training, the goal of modern nursing training is not only to equip the specialist but also to improve the basic education of all in the field. This effort will result in the extended application of mental health principles to patients of all types.

The first specialty education in psychiatric nursing, described above, was offered largely at the baccalaureate level. Because teachers and supervisors were in such short supply, the emphasis was on preparation of persons in these categories. Baccalaureate programs offering a specialty in psychiatric nursing grew in number, served their purpose for a brief period, and were discontinued by 1956 as content for masters' programs became clearly delineated, and as basic training in psychiatric nursing was required as an integral part of all baccalaureate programs (Gregg, 1966). Enrollment in graduate programs has progressively increased over the past twenty years. For example, the number of M.A. and M.S. degrees awarded in 1965 was nearly double the number awarded in 1959.

With the advent of opportunity for advanced study came the recognition of the significance of the nurse-patient relationship and its potential for therapeutic interaction as opposed to the traditional or former custodial approach. It also became apparent that there was too little opportunity for clinical work in the advanced programs, and that there was need to incorporate additional content from the social and behavioral sciences in order to define and understand the clinical process in psychiatric nursing.

Early advanced curricula tended to follow the pattern of schools of education, and some of the problems of education as well as the benefits were borrowed in this association. Initially, programs were inclined to be sketchy in the areas of the clinical major and sciences and richer in administration theory, educational philosophy, teaching methods, curriculum building, and teaching and administrative practicums. In recent years the clinical emphasis in the programs has been strengthened, and some programs offer a clinical major without formal education in teaching and administration (Gregg, 1966, p. 18).

Table 9 shows the growth in number of schools and training programs

Table 9. Growth in Number of Schools and Training Programs for Nursing: 1945–66 [a]

| Year | TOTAL NURSING SCHOOLS | TRAINING PROGRAM | | |
		Diploma	Associate degree	Bachelor's Degree
1945	1,295	1,157		138
1946	1,271	1,100		171
1947	1,253	N.A.		N.A.
1948	1,245	1,062		183
1949	1,215	1,134		N.A.
1950	1,190	1,118	1	195
1951	1,170	972	N.A.	198
1952	1,155	1,065	N.A.[b]	198
1953	1,125	1,017	21	198
1954	1,124	992	30	215
1955	1,125	967	19	155
1956	1,115	956	20	161
1957	1,118	944	28	166
1958	1,125	935	38	172
1959	1,119	918	48	171
1960	1,123	908	57	172
1961	1,118	883	69	174
1962	1,128	874	84	178
1963	1,142	860	105	183
1964	1,153	840	130	188
1965	1,191	821	174	198
1966	1,219	797	218	210

[a] Data from: NLN, unpublished data; ANA, 1966.
[b] Included with diploma programs.

in nursing since 1945, and reflects current trends in basic nursing education. As new associate-degree and collegiate programs are developing, increasing numbers of diploma programs are closing.

There has been a continued trend toward integration of psychiatric nursing knowledge and social and behavioral science content in the undergraduate curriculum: all collegiate schools of nursing now include teaching of psychiatric-mental health nursing and behavioral science, and provide clinical learning experience geared to orientation and preparation of the nurse for therapeutic nursing care. Clinical psychiatric nursing experience is now required in all diploma programs and in an increasing number of associate-degree programs. As of 1967, there were about 44 graduate programs in psychiatric nursing, which train clinical specialists, teachers, supervisors, administrators, consultants, and research personnel at the master's and doctoral levels, and an additional six such programs are in the developmental stage. Seven of the existing programs have a major in child psychiatric nursing as differentiated from general or adult psychiatric nursing. All but four of the existing graduate programs participate in the NIMH training program for nurses. Table 10 contains information on NIMH support of graduate training programs in psychiatric nursing; the NIMH support program is reflective of the growth of the psychiatric nursing field. There are an estimated 640,000 nurses employed in the United States (Marshall, 1967), who were trained in the three types of programs described earlier. A number of these are psychiatric nurses by virtue of on-the-job or inservice training or in combination with short-term training of one sort or another. The American Nurses' Association has conducted several national inventories of nurses. The 1962 inventory (Marshall and Moses, 1965) was the first of these to attempt to obtain specific information on educational background, psychiatric specialization, and areas of clinical practice. In this study, however, it was possible to obtain such data on nurses in fewer than one third of the states. A new, more inclusive inventory is expected to be completed by the end of 1967 (Marshall, 1967). A 1963 NIMH study of personnel in approximately 2,000 mental health establishments identified over 18,000 nurses employed in outpatient psychiatric clinics, hospitals

Table 10. NIMH Support of Training Programs in Psychiatric Nursing: 1948–66 [a]

NUMBER OF GRANTS AWARDED

| FISCAL YEAR | BACCALAUREATE PROGRAMS | | Master's and doctoral programs |
	Basic collegiate	Advanced psychiatric nursing [b,c]	
1948		5	4
1949		9	5
1950		11	5
1951		13	6
1952		13	9
1953		15	9
1954		13	10
1955		13	12
1956	2	13	13
1957	39	13	16
1958	64	10	19
1959	71		25
1960	72		24
1961	85		28
1962	99		36
1963	103		41
1964	122		41
1965	122		38
1966	124		40

[a] NIMH, unpublished data.
[b] Programs leading to baccalaureate degree for graduates of diploma schools.
[c] NIMH support ended in 1958.

Table 11. Total Number of Nurses Employed in Mental Health Establishments by Age and Sex, and Percentage Distribution of Nurses by Age, Sex, and Level of Education: 1963 [a]

SEX AND AGE	NUMBER OF RESPONDENTS	PERCENTAGE BY HIGHEST LEVEL OF EDUCATION						
		Total	Less than 3-year diploma	3-year diploma	Bachelor's	Graduate study but no degree	Graduate degree	Unspecified
Sex								
Male	1,227	100.0	6.7	56.8	14.8	14.6	6.7	0.4
Female	16,686	100.0	3.5	72.4	11.2	9.0	3.4	0.5
Age								
25	1,872	100.0	3.4	78.2	14.5	3.5	0.1	0.3
25–34	4,607	100.0	3.3	72.2	14.6	7.5	2.1	0.3
35–44	4,474	100.0	3.4	69.1	12.2	10.3	4.7	0.3
45–54	4,436	100.0	4.4	68.9	9.0	12.0	5.1	0.6
55–64	2,195	100.0	4.1	72.6	7.0	11.1	4.4	0.8
65+	301	100.0	4.0	76.9	3.7	11.0	2.7	1.7
Total respondents	18,010	100.0	3.7	71.1	11.4	9.3	3.6	0.9

a Eldridge, 1965a, p. 2, Table 3.

for the mentally ill, and institutions for the mentally retarded (Eldridge, 1965a).

A 1950 study conducted by the National League for Nurses indicated that there were fewer than 10,000 graduate nurses employed in psychiatric facilities (Nowakowski, 1950). Table 11 shows the distribution by age, sex, and level of education of the 18,010 nurses who responded to a survey questionnaire in the 1963 study. Over 71 per cent of these nurses had attained the three-year diploma, 11 per cent had bachelor's degrees, more than 9 per cent had graduate schooling but no graduate degree, and 3.6 per cent had graduate degrees, including nine with doctorates. Obviously, formal advanced specialty training in psychiatric nursing is not in the background of the great majority of these nurses. The group had spent on the average eight years in nonmental health nursing and nine years in mental health nursing.

Today a pressing issue in psychiatric nursing education is, as indeed it is in all of the mental health disciplines, the incorporation of instruction for functioning in comprehensive community mental health settings. Between 1956 and 1963, graduate psychiatric nursing was primarily concerned with the development of basic clinical skills. During this period most master's programs were extended from one year to one and a half to two years, and provided increasingly intensive training for psychotherapeutic nursing.

In 1963, when the Community Mental Health Act was passed, psychiatric nursing educators became concerned with the need for incorporating additional training specifically geared toward preparing nurses for community health services, such as training in community organization and action, program planning, program developments, and development of new approaches to clinical care.

Five years later, psychiatric nursing is well on its way toward incorporating these goals. Community mental health content is rapidly being incorporated in all master's programs in psychiatric-mental health nursing. In addition, two post-master's programs have been developed in community mental health nursing. These programs are geared toward preparing the nurse for functioning in community organizations and for participating in the development of community mental health programs.

As is chronically true of the entire nursing field, psychiatric nursing is plagued with a shortage of manpower. Current efforts are being made to extend the effectiveness of the trained nurse through the use of aides, technicians, and other personnel whose training requires shorter periods of time.

CONCLUDING REMARKS

The preceding discussions of the more traditional disciplines of psychiatry, clinical psychology, social work, and psychiatric nursing were intended as a vehicle for tracing the major developmental aspects of the mental health field to date. It is certainly not considered a complete coverage, since there are other groups performing vital roles that are part of the complete picture of the current scene. Many of these professions and occupational groups, such as the hospital aides, occupational therapists, recreational therapists, etc., have traditionally played a major mental health role. As the complexities of mental health are increasingly incorporated into public awareness and policy, the ramifications of its principles create increasing demands for manpower over an ever-expanding range of professions and occupations. One of the emphases of the Joint Commission on Mental Illness and Health in 1959 was that new occupations and professional groups needed to be developed along with the extension of the mental health involvement of teachers, lawyers, police, clergy, and other existing professions. Such programs have since been instituted along with programs for the training of nonprofessionals and subprofessionals who are completely new to the mental health scene.

While much of the manpower discussion and the professions that have been mentioned are primarily those involved with the delivery of treatment, care, and services to the population, tremendous growth has also occurred in those fields devoted to human behavioral research. Whereas at one time research on mental health and illness was primarily conducted by psychologists and psychiatrists, almost the total spectrum of scientific fields is now included. Sociology and anthropology are increasingly involved in mental health issues; the biological sciences continue to bridge the gap between man's internal organic milieu and his psychosocial functioning. New areas, such as behaviorial genetics, sociobiology, and psychochemistry, have emerged, along with training programs that train biological scientists of all persuasions in the dimension of behavior. There continue to be, however, critical shortages of, and increased competition among the sciences for, qualified students under the pressures of the nation's total needs for trained scientists.

As is true with all health services, and as was initially noted by the Joint Commission (1961), manpower supply remains the key to all health services, since "how rapidly and how well manpower is developed essentially determines how rapidly health services rise" (Heistand, 1966, p. 146). Thus, the paradox is that although health services in general, and mental health services in particular, have grown at a remarkable rate, the apparent need is for ever more manpower and services to meet the minimal standards set by professional judgment and to keep pace with a rapidly growing population. It is in this very context, however, that long-standing, difficult conceptual and social issues need be addressed, both to permit evaluation of what has been and is being done, as well as to give realistic understanding of what can be accomplished in the foreseeable future.

A major unresolved problem that continues to plague the field is the lack of even reasonably precise definitions or conceptions of the terms "mental illness" and "mental health." While the term "mental health" is often used in a euphemistic fashion interchangeably with "mental illness," the usage has become increasingly broad over the years, further increasing the definitional problem from what it was when evaluated by Jahoda for the Joint Commission in 1958. For some it appears to be synonymous with human behavior in total, and, therefore, becomes such a broad penumbra that its use for science or for other than the most gross description becomes nil.

The definitional issues are not mere academic exercises but are fundamental to clarification of the parameters of involvement of the mental health professionals, and are essential for the establishment of basic goals for the measurement of program effectiveness. As our understanding of the sociopsychological factors in all aspects of society and culture increases, and as public acceptance of these concepts grows, demand for mental health services to deal with ever increasing problems of the population grows. An estimated 1,750,000 serious crimes are committed a year, 50,000 people are estimated to be addicted to the use of drugs, and some 4,000,000 persons are problem drinkers (GAP, 1964). Viewed as evidence of disturbed psychological behavior, such social problems demand attention, and the mental health professions have come to view them, and many others, as mental health problems. This places increasing and staggering demands upon already overtaxed manpower resources attempting to deal with the traditional types of mental illness.

These are broad social issues, but whether it is meaningful or even appropriate to view them in the context of illness and health is a matter that has been receiving increased attention in the past few years (Albee, 1967a, 1967b; Dunham, 1965; Redlich, 1967; Szasz, 1961, 1963). Acceptance of alternate models for viewing these various behavioral manifestations may require a completely different set of manpower requirements and alter the mental health demand picture in a significant manner.

At the beginning of the report, *Current Concepts of Positive Mental Health,* Jahoda (1958) quoted Adolph Meyer, whose 1925 comments on health are as appropriate today as they were then. In essence, Meyer states that there are two approaches to health: the utopian way, which leads to moralizing, and the scientific way, which leads to experimentation and deliberate action. At this junction in time it still appears, as Jahoda noted in 1958, that no final choice has yet been made.

In a very short period of time the mental health field and its attendant professions have grown at an unprecedented rate. Trained manpower has always been a prime concern, and increasing effort continues to be devoted to its production and, more recently, to its utilization. The previous sections of this chapter have been devoted to the growth of the field and its major professions in order to provide a data backdrop of manpower development. Many issues, however, remain unresolved, partially addressed, and even ignored under the pressures of growth, development, research, and multiplying demands for delivery of services to those in need. While the importance of the past and continuing efforts directed toward manpower production is not to be denied, the time is propitious for a proper perspective on the locus of manpower problems in the total scheme of things. As has been stated before (Arnhoff, 1968a, 1968b, 1968c; David, 1966), manpower concerns are the last, not the first, steps in the mental health conceptual chain; rational planning, assessment, and future directions follow only from prior specification of goals and resources. The current and continuing American social welfare revolution makes it mandatory that this be done. The following chapters represent a directed focus on these major, critical issues, and will place mental health and mental health manpower in a broader perspective by discussing in detail the conceptual, social, economic, and political issues only alluded to here.

REFERENCES

ALBEE, G. W. 1959. *Mental health manpower trends*. New York: Basic Books.
————. 1967a. Needed: A conceptual breakthrough. In *Mental health manpower—Volume II. Recruitment, Training and Utilization*. Sacramento: California Dept. of Mental Hygiene.
————. 1967b. The relation of conceptual models to manpower needs. In E. L. Cowen, E. A. Gardner, and M. Zax (Eds.), *Emergent approaches to mental health problems*. New York: Appleton-Century-Crofts.
American Medical Association. 1967. Medical education in the United States. *Journal of the American Medical Association, 202*: 725–832.
American Nurses' Association. *Facts about nursing: a statistical summary*. New York: ANA.
American Psychiatric Association. 1952. *Psychiatry and medical education*. Report of the 1951 Conference on Psychiatric Education, Cornell University, June 1951. Washington, D.C.: APA.
American Psychiatric Association. 1953. *The psychiatrist: his training and development*. Report on the 1952 Conference on Psychiatric Education, Cornell University, June 1952. Washington, D.C.: APA.
American Psychiatric Association. 1967. *Membership directory, 1967*. Washington, D.C.: APA.
APPEL, K. E., and H. H. MORRIS, JR. 1963. Psychiatry. In A. Deutsch and H. Fishman (Eds.), *The encyclopedia of mental health*. Vol. 5. New York: Franklin Watts.
ARNHOFF, F. N. 1968a. The Boston mental health survey: a context for interpretation. In W. J. Ryan *et al.* (Eds.), *Distress in the city: essays on the design and administration of metropolitan mental health services*. Cleveland: Case Western Reserve University Press.
————. 1968b. Realities and mental health manpower. *Mental Hygiene, 52*:181–189.
————. 1968c. Reassessment of the trilogy—need, supply, demand. *American Psychologist, 23*:312–316.

———, and B. M. SHRIVER. 1966. *A study of the current status of mental health personnel supported under National Institute of Mental Health training grants.* Public Health Service Publication No. 1541. Washington, D.C.: U.S. Government Printing Office.

BARTON, W. E., and W. MALAMUD. 1964. Preface. In D. W. Hammersley (Ed.), *Training the psychiatrist to meet changing needs.* Report on the Conference on Graduate Psychiatric Education, Washington, D.C., December 1962. Washington, D.C.: APA.

BENNETT, C. C., L. S. ANDERSON, S. COOPER, L. HASSOL, D. KLEIN, and G. ROSENBLUM. 1966. *Community psychology.* Report of the Boston Conference on the Education of Psychologists for Community Mental Health. Boston: Boston University.

BERKMAN, T. D. 1953. *Practice of social workers in psychiatric hospitals and clinics.* New York: American Association of Psychiatric Social Workers.

BLANK, L. 1964. Clinical psychology training, 1945–1962: Conferences and issues. In L. Blank and H. P. David (Eds.), *Sourcebook for training in clinical psychology.* New York: Springer.

BOEHM, W. W. 1959. *Objectives of the social work curriculum of the future.* Vol. 1. *The comprehensive report of the curriculum study.* New York: Council on Social Work Education.

BRAND, J. L. 1968. The United States: a historical perspective. In R. H. Williams and L. D. Ozarin (Eds.), *Community mental health: an international perspective.* San Francisco: Jossey-Bass.

BRAYFIELD, A. H. 1967. Psychology—manpower fact sheet. Washington, D.C.: American Psychological Association.

COMPTON, B. E. 1966. Psychology's manpower: characteristics, employment, and earnings. *American Psychologist,* 21:224–229.

CONLEY, R. W., M. CONWELL, and M. B. ARRILL. 1967. An approach to measuring the cost of mental illness. *American Journal of Psychiatry,* 124:755–762.

COWEN, E. L., E. A. GARDNER, and M. ZAX. (Eds.). 1967. *Emergent approaches to mental health problems.* New York: Appleton-Century-Crofts.

———, and M. ZAX. 1967. The mental health fields today: issues and problems. In E. L. Cowen, E. A. Gardner, and M. Zax (Eds.), *Emergent approaches to mental health problems.* New York: Appleton-Century-Crofts.

DAVID, H. 1966. *Reflections on manpower utilization.* Mental Health Manpower Current Statistical and Activities Report No. 11. Chevy Chase, Md.: NIMH.

DEUTSCH, A. 1948. *The shame of the states.* New York: Harcourt-Brace.

DE VERA, R. (Ed.). 1967. *Statistics on social work education, November 1, 1966 and academic year 1965–1966.* New York: Council on Social Work Education.

DUNHAM, H. W. 1965. Community psychiatry: the newest therapeutic bandwagon. *Archives of General Psychiatry,* 12:303–313.

ELDRIDGE, M. D. 1965a. *Selected characteristics of nurses employed in mental health establishments, 1963.* Mental Health Manpower Current Statistical and Activities Report No. 7. Chevy Chase, Md.: NIMH.

———. 1965b. *Survey of mental health establishments—staffing patterns and survey methodology.* Mental Health Manpower Current Statistical and Activities Report No. 8. Chevy Chase, Md.: NIMH.

EWALT, J. R. 1959. Staff review. In G. W. Albee, *Mental health manpower trends.* New York: Basic Books.

FEIN, R. 1967. *The doctor shortage.* Washington, D.C.: Brookings Institution.

FRENCH, D. G. 1964. *Needed research on social work manpower.* Report to the Task Force on Social Work Education and Manpower, Washington, D.C.: HEW.

GREGG, D. n.d. Trends in graduate education in psychiatric nursing, emphasizing need for the clinical specialist. In H. Kohler (Ed.), *Psychiatric concepts in public health nursing.* Conference report, Minneapolis, October, 1966. Minneapolis: University of Minnesota School of Public Health.

GROB, G. N. 1966. The state mental hospital in mid-nineteenth-century America: a social analysis. *American Psychologist,* 21:510–523.

Group for the Advancement of Psychiatry (GAP). 1948. *Report on medical education.* GAP Report No. 3. New York: GAP.

GAP. 1962. *The preclinical teaching of psychiatry.* GAP Report No. 54. New York: GAP.

GAP. 1964. *Medical practice and psychiatry: the impact of changing demands.* GAP Report No. 58. New York: GAP.

GRUENBERG, E. 1967. Discussion of Dr. Frank Riessman's paper. In M. Greenblatt, P. E. Emery, and B. C. Glueck, Jr. (Eds.), *Poverty and mental health.* Psychiatric Research Report No. 21. Washington, D.C.: APA.

HEISTAND, D. L. 1966. Research into manpower for health service. *Milbank Memorial Fund Quarterly,* 44 (4):146–181.

House of Representatives. Eighty-ninth Congress. Interstate and Foreign Commerce Committee. 1965. Hearings on research facilities, mental health staffing, continuation of health programs, and group practice bills. Washington, D.C.: U.S. Government Printing Office.

JAHODA, M. 1958. *Current concepts of positive mental health.* New York: Basic Books.

Joint Commission on Mental Illness and Health. 1961. *Action for mental health.* New York: Basic Books.

KIDNEIGH, J. C. 1965. History of American social work. In H. L. Lurie (Ed.), *Encyclopedia of social work.* New York: National Association of Social Workers.

LEIGHTON, A. 1967. Is social environment the cause of psychiatric disorder? In R. R. Monroe, G. D. Klee, and E. B. Brody (Eds.), *Psychiatric epidemiology and mental health planning.* Psychiatric Research Report No. 22. Washington, D.C.: APA.

LOCKMAN, R. F. 1966. *Occupational and personal characteristics of psychiatrists in the United States—1965.* Mental Health Manpower Current Statistical and Activities Report No. 9. Chevy Chase, Md.: NIMH.

MARSHALL, E. D. (Ed.). 1967. *Facts about nursing: a statistical summary.* New York: ANA.

———, and E. B. MOSES. 1965. *The nation's nurses: inventory of professional registered nurses.* New York: ANA.

National Academy of Sciences. 1967. *Doctorate recipients from United States Universities, 1958–1966.* Publication No. 1489. Washington, D.C.: NAS.

National Institute of Mental Health (NIMH), Division of Manpower and Training Programs. 1965a. *Selected characteristics of psychologists employed in mental health establishments, 1963.* Mental Health Manpower Current Statistical and Activities Report No. 4. Chevy Chase, Md.: NIMH.

NIMH, Division of Manpower and Training Programs. 1965b. *Selected characteristics of social workers.* Mental Health Manpower Current Statistical and Activities Report No. 6. Chevy Chase, Md.: NIMH.

NIMH, Division of Manpower and Training Programs. 1966. *Psychologists in mental health: based on the 1964 National Register of the National Science*

Foundation. Public Health Service Publication No. 1557. Washington, D.C.: U.S. Government Printing Office.

NIMH, Division of Manpower and Training Programs. 1967. *Mental health training and manpower, 1968–1972.* Chevy Chase, Md.: NIMH.

National Science Foundation (NSF), Office of Economic and Manpower Studies. 1965. *Salaries and professional characteristics of U.S. scientists, 1964.* Report of the National Register of Scientific and Technical Personnel. NSF No. 64–27. Washington, D.C.: U.S. Government Printing Office.

NSF, Office of Economic and Manpower Studies. 1966. *Salaries and selected characteristics of U.S. scientists, 1966.* Report of the National Register of Scientific and Technical Personnel. NSF No. 66–34. Washington, D.C.: U.S. Government Printing Office.

NOWAKOWSKI, A. J. 1950. *Inventory and qualifications of psychiatric nurses: report on the questionnaire study of the psychiatric nursing project of the National League of Nursing Education, April, 1950.* New York: NLNE.

PECK, C. P., and E. ASH. 1964. Training in the Veterans Administration. In L. Blank and H. P. David (Eds.), *Sourcebook for training in clinical psychology.* New York: Springer.

PEPLAU, H. E. 1958. Educating the nurse to function in psychiatric services. In Southern Regional Education Board, *Nursing personnel for mental health programs.* Report of the Conference in Mental Health Training and Research, Wagoner, Oklahoma, March 1957. Atlanta: SREB.

RAIMY, V. C. (Ed.). 1950. *Training in clinical psychology.* New York: Prentice-Hall.

REDLICH, F. C. 1967. Discussion of Dr. H. Jack Geiger's paper. In M. Greenblatt, P. E. Emory, and B. C. Glueck, Jr. (Eds.), *Poverty and mental health.* Psychiatric Research Report No. 21. Washington, D.C.: APA.

RIDENOUR, N. 1961. *Mental health in the United States: a fifty-year history.* Cambridge, Mass.: Harvard University Press.

ROBERTS, M. M. 1963. *American nursing: history and interpretation.* New York: Macmillan.

ROMANO, J. 1967. Psychiatry, the university, and the community. In E. L. Cowen, E. A. Gardner, and M. Zax (Eds.), *Emergent approaches to mental health problems.* New York: Appleton-Century-Crofts.

RUBINSTEIN, E. A., and M. LORR (Eds.). 1954. *Survey of clinical practice in psychology.* New York: International Universities.

SANTOS, E. H., and E. STAINBROOK. 1949. A history of psychiatric nursing in the nineteenth century. *Journal of the History of Medicine and Allied Science,* 4:48–74.

SARASON, S. B., M. LEVINE, I. I. GOLDENBERG, D. L. CHERLIN, and E. M. BENNETT. 1966. *Psychology in community settings: clinical, educational, vocational, social aspects.* New York: Wiley.

SCHMITT, M. 1949. Report of development of criteria for the evaluation of advanced programs of study in psychiatric nursing and mental hygiene to the National League of Nursing Education. Unpublished manuscript, New York.

SHAKOW, D. 1947. Recommended graduate training program in clinical psychology. *American Psychologist,* 2:539–558.

SPEISMAN, J. C. 1968. Functional roles and education in psychology. *American Psychologist.* 23:321–324.

STEVENS, L. F., and D. D. HENRIE. 1966. A history of psychiatric nursing. *Bulletin of the Menninger Clinic,* 30:32–38.

STROTHER, C. R. (Ed.). 1956. *Psychology and mental health.* Washington, D.C.: American Psychological Association.

SZASZ, T. S. 1961. *The myth of mental illness.* New York: Hoeber-Harper.

———. 1963. *Law, liberty and psychiatry.* New York: Macmillan.

TURNER, R. J., and J. CUMMING. 1967. Theoretical malaise and community mental health. In E. L. Cowen, E. A. Gardner, and M. Zax (Eds.), *Emergent approaches to mental health problems.* New York: Appleton-Century-Crofts.

TYLER, F. B., and J. C. SPEISMAN. 1967. An emerging scientist-professional role in psychology. *American Psychologist,* 22:839–847.

U.S. Bureau of the Census. 1966. *Current population reports: population estimates.* Series P–25, No. 331. Washington, D.C.: U.S. Government Printing Office.

U.S. Bureau of the Census. 1967. *Current population reports: population estimates.* Series P–25, No. 359. Washington, D.C.: U.S. Government Printing Office.

U.S. Health, Education, and Welfare Department. 1965. *Closing the gap in social work manpower.* Report of the Departmental Task Force on Social Work Education and Manpower. Washington, D.C.: U.S. Government Printing Office.

U.S. Health, Education, and Welfare Department, National Center for Health Statistics. 1966. *Health resources statistics, 1965.* Public Health Service Publication No. 1509. Washington, D.C.: U.S. Government Printing Office.

U.S. Labor Department, Bureau of Labor Statistics. 1964. *Employment outlook for social workers.* Occupational Outlook Report Series, Bulletin 1375–43. Reprinted from the 1963–64 Occupational Outlook Handbook. Washington, D.C.: U.S. Government Printing Office.

WATSON, R. I. 1953. A brief history of clinical psychology. *Psychological Bulletin,* 50:321–346.

WEBSTER, T. G. 1967. Psychiatry and behavioral science curriculum time in U.S. schools of medicine and osteopathy. *Journal of Medical Education,* 42:687–696.

WILTE, E. F., K. A. KENDALL, and E. V. HOLLIS. 1955. Education for social work. In L. E. Blanch (Ed.), *Education for the professions.* Washington, D.C.: U.S. Government Printing Office.

ZILBOORG, G., and G. W. HENRY. 1941. *A history of medical psychology.* New York: Norton.

CHAPTER 2

A Perspective on Manpower
Theory and Conceptualization

HENRY DAVID

I

MY REMARKS, AS YOU WILL have discerned from the title they bear, are intended by the organizers of this symposium to be propaedeutic. However, it is far from clear what the structure of "introductory knowledge" or the content of "preliminary instruction" in the manpower field either is or should be. I may note, parenthetically, that lack of clarity on this score created problems for the recent interdisciplinary Symposium on Manpower Theory and Policy Issues sponsored by the Commission on Human Resources and Advanced Education (1966).

The characteristics of the manpower field, for practical purposes, are formed by a combination of research activities and policy problems, concerns, and issues. Specialists from a variety of disciplines operate in it with the analytical tools, research techniques, conceptual models, predilections, and insights characteristic of their particular sciences. The field patently still lacks a coherent or integrated body of theory, but does exhibit a large number of flourishing hypotheses that invite testing. Interdisciplinary approaches to the development of theory are still at a rudimentary level. The variety of research activities in the field has produced a large and varied body of empirical findings, but they do not yet appear to be significantly cumulative. It is a field in which active scholars proclaim the need for more research on a series of quite fundamental problems in which the relationship of theory to policy is tenuous, and in which efforts to evaluate the consequences of policies and programs are far fewer than they should be. It is even in its more sophisticated aspects a very young field indeed.

If these observations and judgments appear extreme or unduly mordant, I readily grant that some discounting of some of them may be in order. Moreover, I hope that this symposium will demonstrate that I have been guilty of exaggeration. However, I venture to submit them in order to discourage any expectation that I am about to provide a neatly packaged kit of all-purpose "introductory knowledge to the art or science of manpower."

What I have to offer might be titled "A Clutch of General Propositions, Suggestive Suppositions, Monitory Observations, Occasional Facts, and Instructive Lessons Presumed To Be Relevant to Reflecting on Selected Manpower Issues in the Mental Health Field!" I realize that this title might register a claim to descriptive power but not to elegance. I also realize that much of what I will have to say may provoke displeasure. Some of it will appear to manpower specialists too elementary and commonplace to warrant iteration. And I have no doubt that mental health specialists will be appalled by my ignorance in their field of expertise.

II

It may be instructive to begin with the U.S. Department of Labor *Report on Manpower Requirements, Resources, Utilization, and Training*, which accompanies the *Manpower Report of the President* (1967). The terms in the title of the first of these reports mirror the concerns of manpower policies, the objectives of manpower programs, and major target areas of current manpower research. These terms represent a substantial part of what may be called the conceptual language in the manpower field. If, to these terms, the words "demand" and "supply," "shortages" and "surpluses," "education" and "development," and "occupational choice" are added, the basic vocabulary of what may be called "manpowerese" is virtually rounded out.

The Department of Labor report (1967) observes that shortages of varying "intensity" were "reported in a wide range of occupations" in different parts of the country in 1966; that among the most serious were some involving scientific and professional workers, and that stringencies were especially acute among "health service workers." It notes that "the long-term need for personnel in human service professions [within which mental health manpower falls] has become more acute during the

past few years," in large part because of "the advent of Great Society programs . . ." (p. 151). The report also notes: "Widespread shortages are
reported in all the major health professions and in many supporting professions" (p. 165), and records shortages in psychiatric and medical social
work.

Declaring that available health services "are now being adversely affected in both quantity and quality by shortages" (p. 187), the report
states that the "health service industry," which employed some 3.7 million workers in 1966, is "one of the largest sources of employment in the
national economy" (p. 187). It is estimated that by 1975 this industry
will employ a total of 5.4 million workers.

According to the report, the likelihood is that shortages will continue
to plague the health service industry in the future, in spite of present
and contemplated efforts to expand significantly the supplies of new
personnel. It estimates, for example, that "the number of new physicians
needed will average about 15,600 per year between 1966 and 1975"
(p. 188), and that the "number of new nurses required per year . . .
will average about 43,000" (p. 189) over the same period.

The Department of Labor report serves several useful purposes. It directs attention to such key notions as "shortages," "requirements," and
"needs," on each of which I will comment shortly. More important, it
underscores the fruitfulness of perceiving both the demand and supply
problems associated with any particular occupation or cluster of functionally related occupations, and the policies and programs designed to
resolve them, within a larger context. This understanding was clearly
present in Dr. George W. Albee's (1959) pathbreaking study, *Mental
Health Manpower Trends*, which emphasized the relationship of mental
health personnel shortages to the array of problems affecting the nation's
resources of scientific and professional manpower, deficiencies in the nation's educational system, the character of the society's dominant value
system, and to still other large considerations.

III

The state of the art of manpower policy-making may still be in its infancy.
However, it is armed with one important piece of knowledge gleaned
from experience. We have learned that to approach a manpower problem associated with a particular segment of the labor force as if it exists
in isolation is an invitation to adopt irrelevant or self-defeating solutions. Elsewhere (David, 1965), in commenting on the strong tendency
toward fragmentation in manpower policy formation, I urge the cultivation of the habit of searching for interrelations and interconnections. I
hasten to admit, of course, that this, like other virtuous habits, is more
easily proclaimed than acquired. The bias toward fragmentation, I observed, meant:

It took those concerned much longer than necessary during the 1950's to learn that at least part of the shortage of engineers could be more accurately identified as a shortage of supporting personnel—of technicians, draftsmen, and engineering aides. Similarly delayed was the understanding that the demand for and supply of physicians could not be dissociated from the availability and functions of nurses, technicians, and other paramedical personnel. The teaching profession came slowly to a realization that there might be other ways of meeting the rising demands for its services in addition to increasing the supply of qualified teachers.

Fragmentation in the area of manpower policy . . . reflects differentiated needs and interests, as well, frequently as shortsightedness and a failure of understanding. Many specialized manpower needs would not be recognized if they were not separately represented. It is also understandable that the advocates of particular policies press them vigorously, and that they sometimes appear less concerned with the easing or solution of a manpower problem than with the particular mechanism to be used.

Such normal manifestations of human . . . behavior, however, tend to deny the interrelatedness of manpower problems and ignore consequences that the pursuit of one policy may have upon others. Thus, if incentives are established to encourage the flow of more young men and women into science and engineering, the stream moving toward careers in medicine may diminish. If efforts are made to assure that demands for medically trained researchers are met, fewer M.D.'s may be engaged in the practice of medicine. If postgraduate study is widely supported by public and private funds for traineeships, colleges and universities may be deprived of needed teaching personnel. It is difficult to imagine that under conditions of less than full employment, separate policies aimed at improving employment opportunities for older workers, for youth, for members of minority groups, for women, and for the physically handicapped do not, at least in some measure, compete with one another (pp. 101–103).

Fragmentation in the perception of manpower problems and of consequent policy and program approaches has been present in the mental health field. It is also essential in this context to recognize that the goals of mental health may be described as uncertain or open-ended, and that reliable universally accepted measures of progress toward their achievement are lacking. It may also be said that "Balkanization" characterizes the distribution of responsibility for mental health functions and services. These circumstances, it strikes me, conspire to frustrate the design of comprehensive strategies for the effective development, deployment, and utilization of manpower resources. These circumstances, however, should also serve to deter the ready purchase of paper solutions in aggregate statistical terms for imbalances in manpower demand-supply relations.

I V

The habit of searching for interconnections or interrelations has value outside the manpower area, for it discloses systems of interaction operating between policies and programs that have manpower purposes and those that have quite different primary objectives.

Take, for example, the public sector alone, where the major governmental influences upon manpower development and utilization are exercised through policies and programs in the four areas of education, research and development, health, and national security. "Only part of the governmental influence, however, is exercised through these four policy areas. A vast number of other governmental functions, policies, and services, as well as the behavior of governments as employers, affects the development and use of manpower, either directly or indirectly. Governmental mechanisms essentially designed to serve other purposes may be used as a means for achieving manpower ends" (National Manpower Council, 1964, p. 399). It should not be necessary to demonstrate that governmental actions concerned with stability, change, and growth in the economy, or with income levels and distribution, have a strong bearing upon manpower development and utilization. Agricultural, immigration, foreign trade, and taxation policies, as well as those affecting labor standards, labor-management relations, or occupational licensing, for example, also have significant manpower implications.

Clearly, policies in neither the public nor the private sector are maintained in leak-proof containers simply because they are given descriptive or categorical labels reflecting their intended primary purposes. Policies, as well as their programmatic manifestations, not only interact but also have secondary and frequently wholly unintended consequences of great importance.

One way of illustrating where one may be led by the idea of a policy interaction is to pose the following questions: To what degree may the newer educational programs of a compensatory character, the various antipoverty measures, the newer directions in urban policy, and the efforts to improve the quality of man's environments be regarded as second-order mental health programs? If it appears that they are likely to produce nontrivial improvements in the mental health of the population, what implications could such effects have for the character of mental health manpower-resource requirements and their utilization? A subquestion flowing from the preceding one might take the following form: Would more sophisticated, effectively administered Head Start programs or the adoption of a negative income tax lead to downward revisions of the estimates of the personnel required for mental health functions and services in the future?

Obviously, I hope that no one will leap from these questions, which are designed to illustrate the notion of policy interaction, to the conclusion that I am proposing new solutions to manpower problems in the mental health field. These questions are set forth only to sharpen the point that both mental health policies and the manpower policies associated with them should be perceived within the contexts of larger policy structures.

I do not want to minimize how enormously difficult it would be to establish fruitful connections between mental health policies and programs and those in other areas. On this count a venturesome paper, "Social Science and the Elimination of Poverty," by Professor Martin Rein (1967), is very suggestive. From it, moreover, the implications for manpower requirements and utilization of the state of knowledge in a field may also be sensed, as the following quotations from Rein's paper indicate:

Most social scientists seem singularly uninterested in the effects of want and deprivation on the psychology of the poor. . . (p. 146).

Although the literature seldom deals directly with deprivation, a number of hypotheses can be developed which deal with the impact of deprivation and insufficiency on health . . . (p. 147). Consider the body of literature on stress which also attempts to link insufficiency and ill health. Here again the evidence is unclear. . . (p. 148).

In summary . . . , (the various) . . . hypotheses (reviewed) concern the direct and indirect effects on health of deprivation, adversity, and insufficiency, viewing them as sufficient conditions for strain and stress in the body which in turn causes breakdown. But there is also an extensive literature which suggests that hardship seems to lead to stress only under certain social conditions. Impoverishment by itself may have little adverse effect and may not lead to stress. . . (p. 149).

Insufficient income may serve as a stimulant to promote incentive, but where the disparity between needs and income grows too wide it leads to despair and abandonment of the struggle for self-maintenance. . . . Several conflicting hypotheses have been developed to account (for the asserted concentration of mental illness among the poor) . . . (p. 150).

Given the ambiguities surrounding the objectives of mental health and the infirmities of social and behavioral science knowledge about critical aspects of poverty, the task of identifying productive modes of policy interaction is extraordinarily difficult at this point in time. This, however, serves to enlarge the burdens placed upon mental health policies and programs per se and, consequently, to intensify problems on the manpower resources side.

V

Earlier, I cited current information on manpower shortages in the "health service industry." Proponents of programs designed to improve the mental health of the American people, as well as those who seek to remedy grave deficiencies in the care and treatment of the mentally ill, have, of course, long been obsessed with endemic shortages of personnel. Those who have been assessing demand and supply relationships through untinted glasses have not been optimistic that these shortages will be relieved even over the longer pull (Joint Commission, 1961, pp. 140–165). It is appropriate, consequently, to consider the ideas of mental health "needs" and manpower requirements, and thus help illuminate some of these shortage problems.

To start with, it should be noted that the literature on manpower shows that several meanings are associated with the term "shortages." Because different criteria may stand behind assertions concerning their existence, the term does not refer to a single concept. One criterion invoked, of course, is that of the behavior of the price of labor in a free market. Here, differential upward movements in wages or salaries for specific categories of workers are both the sign of and the presumed remedy for a situation in which demand for a resource runs ahead of the available supply. However, it is also true that:

Noneconomic criteria, such as social need or aspiration, standards of professional service, or conceptions of national security, are also used to make judgments about manpower shortages. One reason for this is the extent to which professional manpower is engaged in providing basic social services, as in the fields of education and health. Moreover, a very large proportion of total professional personnel is employed by public or other nonprofit enterprises which respond more slowly and unevenly to changing labor-market conditions than do profit-seeking enterprises. Where salary schedules are set by law, for example, many difficulties stand in the way of changes which might attract additional personnel. Not the least is the reluctance or inability of communities to translate their expressed desire for adequate educational, health, and other social services into higher taxes and appropriations. Unless this occurs, the demand for personnel is not, in economic terms, an effective one (National Manpower Council, 1957, p. 259).

In the health field generally, the use of noneconomic criteria is reflected in estimates of personnel "requirements" and in numerical expressions of shortages on the basis of unfilled budgeted positions in public and nonprivate enterprises.

Concepts of need are extremely useful, "because," as Kenneth E. Boulding (1966) remarks, "the concept of demand itself has serious weaknesses and limitations" (p. 202). However, as he emphasizes, there is no single concept of need, "and especially no single concept of need for health services" (p. 202). Boulding notes: "One's demand for medical care is what he wants; his need for medical care is what the doctor thinks he ought to have" (p. 203). He goes on to observe that "an increasingly professionalized, socialized, organized structure satisfies what the professional conceives of as needs" (p. 203). While physical health is socially defined within relatively narrow limits, that is not the case with mental health.

Even a surface consideration of the boundaries of the mental health field prompts the thought that the quality of humility and the exercise of self-restraint should be viewed as essential ingredients in social definitions of mental health needs (Boulding, 1966). Take, for example, what I assume is one of several accepted current views of the field as "that area of human endeavor devoted to helping persons with emotional or psychological problems. . . . The field of man's anxieties, depressions, irrational doubts and fears, irresponsibilities, disturbed social relations, maladaptive behavior, disturbed thinking—the field of *psychic* problems of man *as man* . . ." (Mariner, 1967, p. 278).

Within so expansive a frame, the options open to the society in meeting what may appear, on the surface, to be similar conceptions of mental health needs are numerous. Perceptions of needs shape mental health goals, functions, and services, and these in turn establish the basis for claims on resources. These perceptions, of course, are defined and redefined by historical circumstance. "The intensity, the satisfaction, and even the character of human needs, beyond the biological level," writes Herbert Marcuse (1964), "have always been preconditioned. Whether or not the possibility of doing or leaving, enjoying or destroying, possessing or rejecting something is seized as a *need* depends on whether or not it can be seen as desirable and necessary, for the prevailing societal institutions and interests" (p. 4).

The extent to which needs are historically defined appears, of course, in every statement about how they undergo change. Thus, the Surgeon General of the Public Health Service (1966), speaking about increases and other changes in the demands for health services, observed:

Many people are beginning to think of good health as a human right. . . . No longer are we willing to provide only what the people can afford, we hope now to provide what they need. . . . Yesterday, perhaps, we tacitly accepted a very limited challenge—to make health services available to most of the people, most of the time. Today, we aspire and fully intend to make the *best* health services readily accessible to *all* who need them (p. 1).

Providing adequate care and treatment for all mentally ill persons and improving the mental health of the population as a whole are highly valued goals. To oppose their fulfillment is to risk being labeled inhuman. But the indeterminateness, the open-endedness, of these goals poses grave problems when one moves to make explicit the claims they would make on manpower and, of course, on other resources—that is, when one attempts not only to specify but also to justify the quantitative dimensions and the qualitative attributes of the personnel to be deployed and utilized to realize these goals, either over time or at any one point in time.

Clearly, the notion of "adequate care and treatment" is ambiguous; the meaning of "all mentally ill persons" is not self-evident; and operational measures of improvements in mental health do not exist. These very deficiencies encourage rather than deter familiar assertions to the effect that mental disease and the attainment of satisfactory standards of mental health constitute the nation's "number one health problem," and that "in no area of medicine are the problems so formidable, the gap between need and available resources so great, and the general reluctance to face up to the grim realities so pronounced as they are in mental disease" (Greenberg, 1967, p. 22) .

So as not to be misunderstood, I want to make it crystal clear that I am not arguing a case against reducing the burden of human suffering imposed by mental and emotional illness, or against improving the mental health of the population. What I am attempting to do—perhaps too elaborately—is to suggest why it has been so easy in the mental health field to slip, as if the terms were interchangeable, from: (1) ambiguous statements about "need," representing expressions of social aspirations or expectations; to (2) statements about "demand," representing descriptions of labor-market situations; to (3) statements about the "requirements" of manpower and other resources for satisfying needs at a given level under unspecified conditions of utilization.

I stated earlier that the options open to the society for meeting mental health needs are numerous, but I did not make explicit the bearing of this proposition upon manpower requirements. One such option, as René Dubos (1966) puts it, is "to provide man with a sheltered environment in which he is protected as completely as possible from any form of traumatic experience" (p. 38) . Rejecting this prospect, Dubos argues for the maintenance of an environment that provides the "constant stimulation and challenge" essential for the normal development and the health state of "certain important traits of man's nature . . ." (p. 38) . He points out:

Life at constant temperature through air conditioning, learning made effortless through mechanical aids, avoidance of conflicts through social adjustment, are examples of the means by which modern life eliminates or minimizes physiological or psychological effort, but by the same token results in atrophy of man's adaptive mechanisms. While protection from stresses and from effort may add to the pleasure or at least to the comfort of the moment, and while emotional neutrality minimizes social conflicts, the consequences of an excessively sheltered life are certainly unfavorable in the long run (p. 38) .

Two questions leap to the surface: If man needs an environment that provides "constant stimulation and challenge," how would this need affect the social definition of mental health "needs"? What manpower implications would flow from a resulting redefinition of mental health needs? In this case, it would not be unreasonable to postulate that the implications would be minor. However, it is not difficult to conceive of redefinitions of mental health needs that could lead to radical departures from more or less common notions of manpower requirements.

Make, for example, the outrageous supposition that the views of R. D. Laing and his followers had become part of the store of accepted professional knowledge. What would happen in consequence to current conceptions of mental health needs, services, and resource requirements? This group holds that schizophrenia—the disease label for about one fifth of the recent first admissions in public hospitals in the United States—does not exist as a disease entity; that it cannot be treated with existing forms of psychiatric therapy; and that positive values may be assigned to psychotic experiences. One of its members writes: "There is, relatively speaking, something remarkably healthy about the chronic schizophrenic, preoccupied with his inner world, spending the day hunched over the central heating fitting in a decrepit back ward" (Cooper, p. 90).

VI

I have been emphasizing difficulties and uncertainties on the requirements side of an unwritten mental health manpower equation, but not, I believe, without warrant. You will recall that the Joint Commission on Mental Illness and Health (1961) declared: "Mental illness involves so many complexities—biological, chemical, psychological, and social—that we do not presume to present wholly definite conclusions or universally approved recommendations" (p. v).

I take it for granted that the complexities are more visible now than they were when the commission submitted its final report, and that the number of variables that should be taken into account on the requirements side of the equation has, consequently, been augmented.

What about the supply side of the mental health manpower equation? On this score I offer a few broad generalizations in support of a personal bias that the difficulties that stand in the way of producing intended alterations in the quantitative and qualitative characteristics of manpower resources, particularly over the shorter run, consistently tend to be underestimated.

The first set of generalizations bears on the processes involved in manpower development and utilization, on the constraints relating to manpower policies and programs, and on the location of responsibilities for manpower development and utilization. The National Manpower Council (1964) observes:

The manpower resources of the United States, as of every community, are the product of continuing and complex processes about which much remains to be learned—notably about how these processes operate under varying conditions, the importance of each of the factors that enters into them, and the ways in which they interact. But enough is known to make it clear that everything that affects the form and substance of the society's life also has a bearing upon its actual and potential manpower resources. The size and composition of the population, marriage and fertility patterns, the incidence of diseases and mortality rates, the physical features of the land and its natural resources, the state of scientific knowledge and technological know-how, the wealth of the society, its political, social, and economic institutions, its values and ideals, the hopes and fears of its people—all these and still other factors influence manpower development and use.

Just as the life of a dynamic society is marked by continuity and stability as well as by change, so are its resources of manpower and the processes that determine their characteristics. These alter with time and reveal the influence of changing conditions, needs, and purposes. Changes in the society's manpower resources can be—and have been—planned and consciously induced, but this does not mean that significant alterations can be brought about quickly and easily, even when universally desired. . . .

The values and institutions of a free and democratic society set limits to the speed and ease with which changes can be effected in its manpower resources. Such a society relies primarily upon systems of inducement rather than upon coercion to develop its human resources. Except in times of crisis, such a society inhibits the authority of government to allocate manpower. It not only protects but also seeks to expand individual freedom of choice.

In a free and democratic society, the responsibilities for manpower development and utilization are widely distributed and are located in both public and private hands. Consequently, out of the multitude of decisions affecting manpower development and use, there may emerge competing and inconsistent as well as complementary and coherent targets and tendencies.

Every individual in a free and democratic society is an agent in the fashioning of its resources of manpower. The basic unit of the resource is the individual. What each individual does with his life has a bearing upon the characteristics of these resources, regardless of the motives, purposes, and decisions influencing his investment in education and training and his labor force behavior. Private organizations and groups, whether business enterprises, labor unions, or professional societies, also act as independent agents in manpower development and utilization. Their decisions and actions, generally not dictated by awareness of their functions in these respects, inevitably influence the quantitative and qualitative characteristics of the society's manpower resources (pp. 53–54).

These several considerations are linked with at least two features of manpower-planning activities concerned with the matching of supplies to estimated requirements, either current or future. One feature is their understandable focus on statistical aggregates, generally on a national scale. A second is their necessary remoteness from the complex processes and patterns of actual decision-making that shape the quantitative and qualitative characteristics of supplies of specialized personnel.

Because of the first, relatively little attention tends to be given to problems of the distribution of personnel in relation to such distinctive configurations as could be established for differentiated patterns of requirements or utilization. Obviously, a statistical matching in national aggregates of the supplies either of specific segments or of all categories of mental health manpower to estimated requirements does not assure the effective distribution of personnel for desired mental health functions and services.

The second feature throws some light on why personnel shortages appear to persist unrelieved, in spite of the range of specific programs designed to reduce their scale. More important, it helps explain the heavy emphasis upon expanding the stream of young people flowing through secondary school into more advanced levels of formal education as a means of ultimately increasing the supplies of specific categories of mental health personnel. The merits of this policy stance can be argued on a variety of grounds, not the least important of which is that every category of mental health manpower represents a fraction of the total supply in a larger professional or paraprofessional occupation.

However, it cannot be taken for granted that the significant increases sought in the supplies of manpower armed with knowledge and skills utilizable for mental health functions and services will take place simply because the total base of highly educated and trained manpower is being expanded. In fact, as this takes place, the problems of recruitment into competing educational channels and of career and employment choices are probably exacerbated. A case might even be made for the point of view that federal manpower and educational policies and programs, taken as a whole, represent a mechanism for intensifying the play of competitive forces operating at critical stages in the educational and occupational choice processes and in the employment market.

Because the supplies of the various categories of mental health personnel are derived from larger supply streams, the continuing and growing preoccupation with questions of education and training, particularly on the professional level, must be viewed as a healthy development. Because of its historical development, the mental health field invites contending approaches to the education and training of professional personnel engaged in therapeutic functions and services. I am not equipped to enter into any of the several ongoing debates as a partisan. However, I do risk saying as an observer that much of their content seems to turn on questions of professional self-interest and jurisdiction, of status and image, and of the conventions and habits of professional schools. For an outsider, these debates shed more light upon some aspects of the history of professionalization in Western culture than upon the range of alternatives that may exist in the performance of mental health functions and the provision of services. (See, e.g., Mariner, 1967.)

In the mental health field, conceptions of therapeutic functions and tasks and, therefore, of appropriate education and training for them have been derived from the knowledge and skill content of the profession *initially* thought to be best suited to their performance. If the content and organization of the knowledge and skills communicated through formal education and training were rationally rather than historically determined, however, they would be operationally derived from the performance of therapeutic functions and tasks. This, in effect, is the object of proposed radical alterations in existing patterns of professional education and training for mental health activities and services.

To propose major transformations in professional education is, of course, to raise quite fundamental questions about the reach of responsibilities attaching to "those institutions empowered to transmit the knowledge and skills of a profession to its future practitioners and to legitimize the characteristics of professional competence and performance" (David, 1967, p. 8).

The prospect of relieving—not solving—current and prospective manpower supply problems in the mental health field by radically redesigning the content and form of professional education and training strikes me as promising. What the new designs should be, I do not know. But, I can suggest the elementary terms of reference for the effort in the form of three questions: (1) For what functions and tasks does a professional school presumably prepare its students? (2) How are these functions and tasks likely to alter in the future, and how could and should they be changed? (3) What changes in patterns of manpower utilization are made possible by new technologies and resources of paraprofessional personnel?

VII

My remarks on net balance express a bearish attitude on the question of achieving an acceptable fit between stipulated requirements and actual supplies of mental health manpower. My present disposition is to believe that the mental health field will be faced with frustrations on this score for years to come. (I refrain from suggesting how one learns to endure these frustrations.)

REFERENCES

ALBEE, G. W. 1959. *Mental health manpower trends.* New York: Basic Books.
BOULDING, K. E. 1966. The concept of need for health services. *Milbank Memorial Fund Quarterly,* 44 (4) :202–225.
COOPER, D. 1967. *Psychiatry and anti-psychiatry.* London: Tavistock.
DAVID, H. 1965. *Manpower policies for a democratic society: the final statement of the National Manpower Council.* New York: Columbia University Press.
———. 1967. Education for the professions: common issues, problems and prospects. *Journal of Education for Social Work,* 3:5–12.
DUBOS, R. 1966. Promises and hazards of man's adaptability. In H. Jarrett (Ed.), *Environmental quality in a growing economy.* Baltimore: Johns Hopkins Press.
GREENBERG, S. 1967. Frontiers beyond Freud. *The Progressive,* 31 (3) :22–25.
Joint Commission on Mental Illness and Health. 1961. *Action for mental health.* New York: Basic Books.
MARCUSE, H. 1964. *One-dimensional man.* Boston: Beacon Press.
MARINER, A. S. 1967. A critical look at professional education in the mental health field. *American Psychologist,* 22:271–281.

National Manpower Council. 1957. *Womanpower*. New York: Columbia University Press.

National Manpower Council. 1964. *Government and manpower*. New York: Columbia University Press.

REIN, M. 1967. Social sciences and the elimination of poverty. *Journal of the American Institute of Planners*, 33 (3) :146–163.

Surgeon General of the United States. Statement before the Special Subcommittee on Education of the House of Representatives, February 18, 1966. (Mimeo.)

Symposium on Manpower Theory and Policy Issues. 1967. Proceedings. *Journal of Human Resources*, 2:140–253.

U.S. Labor Department. 1967. *Manpower report of the President and a report on manpower requirements, resources, utilization, and training*. Washington, D.C.: U.S. Government Printing Office.

CHAPTER 3

The Politics of Mental Health
Objectives and Manpower Assets

HAROLD D. LASSWELL

THE LANGUAGE OF POLITICS

PERHAPS I SHOULD BEGIN with a word about the
political process. To be concerned with politics is to consider patterns of
support, opposition, and indifference on questions of public policy. For
example, we pay attention to formal acts of decision by the electorate, or
by legislators, executives, commission members, and judges. Formal decisions are culminating events in which individuals may play many parts
in connection with political parties, pressure groups, and the various
branches of government.

Public language about policy objectives is relatively abstract, since it
is used to define the overriding goals sought by specific measures, and to
justify concrete proposals. "Mental health" is obviously an abstract expression that can be employed to characterize "preferred events" and to
justify (or attack) particular policies.

When we examine the language of politics, it is possible to discover
the relatively stable terms of general reference used by adherents of the
established order when they are defining their objectives or justifying
(or rejecting) specific policies. The word "ideology" is commonly em-

53

ployed to designate these key symbols, slogans, and statements. At any given time the flow of political communication may be employed at high or low levels of systematization. Political philosophers, jurists, and their functional equivalents are prone to systematic assertions. Presumably, the lay citizen is relatively casual or implicit in his choice of symbols and signs. More often than not a key term or phrase ("life, liberty, and the pursuit of happiness") is an object of sentiment, not of definition.

Nonetheless, political perspectives involve at least some degree of manifest referentiality, no matter how submerged these references may be. In a given body politic the ideology may be the target of one or more counter-ideologies whose spokesmen also differ widely in their levels of systematization. (It is often convenient, when comparing the languages of politics, to use a single term for all rather stable patterns of abstraction, whether "ideology" or "counter-ideology." We join with those who speak of "myth" and define the word to perform this labeling function, and not to stigmatize or glorify the phenomena mentioned.)

There is much uncertainty among scholars and scientists about the influence of abstract language in the political process. At one extreme, the communications initiated by a politician or an administrator may be completely without a demonstrable effect. Such a sequence occurs when legislators, for instance, are suffering from "communication overload" in the prolonged, verbose, and fatiguing debates at the end of a session. So far as votes are concerned, "deals" have already been negotiated, and the public flow of communication is more akin to ritual than manipulation.

The expression "mental health" is no exception to the statement that the effectiveness of abstract words differs from place to place and moment to moment. We shall soon have occasion to consider past trends in this area and to estimate the immediate and the more remote future. When studied in other situations, the language of politics seems to influence how people respond.

From the point of view of a scientific observer, we distinguish between (1) objectives explicitly related to mental health and (2) objectives that affect mental health, though not formulated as such. It is obvious on reflection that programs adopted by official agencies in the name of mental health may cover either more or less than scientific observers define as mental health. These discrepancies are among the most interesting phenomena in the social process of any body politic, since it often happens that a field acquires a publicly accepted significance that far exceeds its importance when seen in the perspective of top specialists.

The present task is to examine present and prospective facts about objectives in the public health sector. The problem is to assess what can be accomplished (1) by invoking the layman's current perspectives and (2) by other tactics. The latter alternative includes attempts to change public demands and expectations relating to mental health. It also covers any effort to influence public health indirectly by strengthening activities in the name of objectives that subordinate (or omit) symbols of reference to mental health.

THE MENTAL HEALTH COMPLEX

A broad area of agreement exists concerning the negative characteristics of mental health, illness, or defect. It is a question of troubled or troublesome people whose behavior is attributed to limitations of the central integrative process. Within this broad zone of agreement, there are significant differences of detail among scientists or laymen. Perhaps the most restrictive definition holds that only those can be said to be ill whose limitations of central process depend on congenital defect or neurological deficiency (chemical, electrical, etc.). Other definitions widen the conception to include sufferers from limitations of primary process (the unconscious). These limitations, expressed as basic emotional conflicts, are believed to depend, for the most part, on the vicissitudes of early individual development. Another view, which is often an attenuation of the second, emphasizes the difficulties of central integration as an expression of unresolved conflicts generated by exposure to confused or contradictory norms of culture. Among laymen much of the troubled and troublesome behavior that fits these categories is perceived as diabolic "possession," or as moral delinquency, hence "criminal." In some societies these behaviors are not always perceived as illness, sin, or crime; rather, they are understood to be instances of supernormality, of superiority (as in some classical cases of epilepsy).

In assessing present and prospective policies related to mental health, it is useful to think about the past, present, and future of (1) mental illness, (2) ideologies regarding mental illness, (3) resource mobilizations (e.g., appropriations) that affect mental illness. We shall label these three interconnected factors the "mental health complex" of a given time or place. As a means of orienting ourselves in regard to the past and future, I propose to offer a developmental construct (a hypothetical model) of the principal features of the mental health complex. This construct is inferred from data about past trends and their conditioning factors; it is also affected by considering the social and political process as a whole.

A DEVELOPMENTAL CONSTRUCT

The most controversial feature of the proposed construct relates to the ideology of mental illness. It is suggested that the scope of the behavior covered by the conception of mental illness has been enlarging; that the extent of this coverage is coming to a climax; that public programs explicitly justified in the name of mental health will gradually decline; that the ideology of cultural reconstruction will, to an increasing extent, guide allocations of manpower resources. The analysis implies that the factors that have contributed to the ideology of mental health in American society are not likely to be replicated in other industrializing societies.

Since our problem is to assess an important social change, it may be useful to comment briefly on the two main modes of change: *ecological* and *executive*. Changes are "ecological" when they go forward with minimum collective guidance. To the extent that they pass through phases of attention, opinion, and action, social changes are "executive." In large-scale advanced industrial societies—of which our own is the prize example—the spread of a science-based technology has a long-term impact on the relative role of the principal modalities of change. It may be noted that executive changes are not entirely "political," if by political is meant the use of political parties, pressure associations, political media of communication, and governmental structures. Some executive changes are accomplished through private rather than official channels. Nevertheless, it is not far wide of the mark to assert that "politicization" is characteristic of the transformation mechanisms of the society that we have in mind.

More specifically, what are the mechanisms of change? How are these related to the mental health complex (the pattern of health and illness, together with professional and lay perspectives on these events)? How are such mechanisms likely to function in the future?

An ecological shift—as in population density—alters the situations in which the various participants in the social process find themselves. Hence the focus of attention is altered, not only in reference to those who are in the immediate environment, but often in regard to the more remote environment. The changing focus of attention evidently helps to stabilize a modified set of expectations, demands, and identities. (Expectations are the matter-of-fact assumptions about past, present, and future events; demands are the outcomes sought; identities are the boundaries of the "self" and "others.") Interacting with the altered perspectives are changed behaviors; in turn, these affect the social and physical environment. The introduction of a science-based technology brings increasing interdependence, and more interdependence raises problems of adjusting competitive or conflicting demands to one another. Specific demands, when promoted with intensity, become part of the political arena, in which parties and other organizations are the means of mobilizing support. Specific demands are justified (or attacked) in general terms relating to doctrinal goals, legal formulas, and popular miranda.[1] Such relatively stable statements, as we have said, are ideologies (or, more generally, "myths"). By "content-analyzing" the flow of political com-

---

1. The miranda are self and other images, the legends, and similar items of popular culture.

munication, it is possible to describe with precision the rise and fall of ideological statements in the political process.

Content analysis can also add precision to our knowledge of any changes that occur in the degree of emphasis given to broad value categories, such as "well-being" (health, safety, comfort), "wealth" (the giving or receiving of claims to the use of resources), and "skill" (the giving or receiving of opportunities to acquire and exercise vocational, professional, and artistic excellence). Other value categories include "power," "enlightenment," "affection," "respect," and "rectitude." Specific demands, such as for a specific appropriation, may be defended (or attacked) in terms of all value categories. Obviously, mental health appropriations may be defended as a means of contributing to well-being. They may also be justified as a means of capital accumulation (wealth) by preventing waste of manpower and of enhancing the pool of talent capable of achieving excellence (skill). Justifications may also be made in terms of national power, asserting that national security calls for mentally competent soldiers. The case may be argued in terms of the advancement of knowledge (enlightenment) as an end in itself, as well as a means to other ends. It may be contended that loving and congenial personal relationships (affection), notably in the family, depend on mental health. The justification may be in "respect" terms, alleging that sound mental health is necessary to achieve and sustain a mobile social order instead of caste. The question may be argued in ethical or religious language (rectitude) of obligation to afford every human being the human dignity of healthy, choosing minds.

The main hypothesis in regard to ideologies is that they are repeated if successful; so, too, are value references. In this way both ideological and value ranks are open to change. Value-ordering has a selective effect; hence, alterations of order, once made, stabilize the new directions of attention, opinion, and action.

PAST TRENDS: THE RISING VALUE EMPHASIS ON WELL-BEING (INCLUDING MENTAL HEALTH)

Content analysis of American party platforms at cross-sections separated by a century shows that value emphases have, indeed, been modified (Namenwirth and Lasswell, in press). I refer to a report on the platforms of each major political party a century ago (1844–64) and more recently (1944–64). For present purposes it suffices to note that considerations of safety, health, and comfort (well-being) have risen. This conclusion holds true of both political parties. It is pertinent to report, although this is not strictly germane to our immediate problem, that ideological changes in the two sets of platforms tended to converge. For example, the stress is increasingly put on "strategies" rather than the "ends" of change.

Three comments are in order: First, it is reasonable to account for this

finding, in part at least, by referring to the decline of family and neighborhood institutions as sources of social (including medical) security,
and the resulting pressure of demand to obtain substitute sources of
value indulgence.

Second, although mental health has not been singled out for a significant degree of mention in national party programs, it has undoubtedly
been a beneficiary of the new acceptance of well-being as an appropriate
goal of national life.

Third, mental health problems have in all probability played a more
influential role in generating change than is reflected in the manifest
content of the platforms. The mental health problems of old people are
particularly disturbing to both the family and the neighborhood; they
far outrun the patience or competence of the environment. The problems of children and young people are equally disturbing in a society
whose outlook is saturated with aspirations for, and realizations of,
middle-class respectability. Upper- and middle-class families feel acutely
humiliated if their offspring fall afoul of police and the courts. They are
disposed to accept the less disturbing view that a "medical" problem is
involved, especially if the frightening terminology of "insane asylums"
can be modified to "mental health clinics," "sanitariums," and the like.

MIDDLE-CLASS SUPPORT OF AN ELITE
OF MEDICINE VERSUS AN ELITE OF FORCE

The middle classes in the United States have had an option of this kind
since they are living in a liberal society. The institutions of the social
order are not governmentalized to the same degree as they are in socialist
states. A distinctive feature of our political process is that congeries of
private groups generate and keep alive demands to circumscribe the
scope of government, especially of central government. In such a non-
totalitarian system, the middle-class strata feel relatively capable of re-
sisting or circumventing the police; hence, the claim of mental illness is
effectively used to strengthen an elite of medicine against an elite of force.

It is commonly asserted, with much justification, that the ideology of
mental illness rises as the ideology of science spreads. In American societies, as in most societies where science is firmly established, traditional
religion is a declining influence. That "demonic" possession could be
successfully alleged by church authorities is most unlikely. Hence, secu-
larism joins with antistatism to favor the rise of a relatively secularized
and independent elite of medicine to cope with troubled and troublesome behavior.

In the United States, in particular, the spread of psychoanalysis (since
the second decade of the twentieth century) has had a strong facilitating
effect on the developments referred to here (Shakow and Rapaport,
1964). The first decade was full of adverse references to nineteenth-

century society. These negative positions were taken by writers who permeated mass as well as elite media of communication. The supposed artificiality, hypocrisy, and prudery of "Victorianism" were standard targets. Thus it was that the predispositions of writers were in a remarkable degree of readiness for psychoanalysis. The channels through which psychoanalysis was disseminated were not primarily medical; nor were they under the control of university departments of psychology. As Shakow and Rapaport (1964) have indicated, psychoanalysis achieved its vogue among elite and mid-elite literary people who created pressures that presently constrained and induced physicians and psychologists alike to concern themselves with fundamental human drives, and especially with manifestations of primary process (the "unconscious" in emotional conflict). With the spread of views attributed to Freud, much troubled and troublesome behavior could be viewed with suspended moral or religious judgment, since it seemed to present a "scientific" or "medical" problem.

PERSISTING NEGATIVE CONNOTATIONS OF ''MENTAL ILLNESS''

In assessing the predispositions whose persistence or attenuation will affect the future, we must not exaggerate the picture whose conspicuous features have been mentioned above. It would be a mistake, for example, to assume that the connotations of "mental health," when referred to in popular or professional circles, have been or remain uniformly positive. This is particularly obvious in connection with the treatment of alleged criminals by courts and penal institutions. In many quarters the impression is growing that "the insanity plea" is grossly misused to enable socially dangerous elements to elude, or to manage an early escape from, custody, and to resume their depredations against life and property. Expectations of this kind help to explain the intensity with which some leaders reinvigorate traditional demands for punitive measures against all law-breakers who are neither "obvious defectives" nor "blithering idiots." To be told that a smooth stock-manipulator is "paranoic" and that a cold-blooded gangster is "sociopathic," with the implication that judges and other decision-makers who act in the name of society ought to treat them more lightly than they otherwise would, is a means of mobilizing indignation, some of which discharges against psychiatrists, judges, and the entire judicial process.

The contemporary picture is further confounded by the discovery made in various jurisdictions by legal counsel devoted to civil rights that the insanity plea, if successful, often leaves the defendant worse off than if it had been omitted. Defendants—and especially poor- or middle-income defendants—may be committed to so-called hospitals for indefinite terms, where they receive no therapy whatever and are often confined under more revolting conditions than prevail in the better prisons.[2] It would seem that legislatures ought to appropriate enough money to enable the hospitals to go beyond custodial to curative aims. But the public image of psychiatrists is not enhanced when superintendents continue year after year to acquiesce in outrageous conditions, and fail to provide the leadership that is required if the latent concern of the community is to be mobilized.

The situation continues to be unsettled because of persisting doubt among judges and other public officials about the appropriate limits of "responsible" or "nonresponsible" conduct, and this doubt, of course, reflects the ambiguities and uncertainties that come to the surface in any society in which the scientific frame of reference is becoming more acceptable. From a scientific point of view, all behavior is perceived as a consequence of constellations of causal factors, which it is the business of the scientist to identify and describe. The concept of responsibility is that, within limits, people can cause their own behavior: by defining objectives; by evaluating the costs, benefits, and risks of alternative strategies; and, finally, by acting in the light of the subjective picture thus clarified. To the modern social scientist and policy-maker, it is obvious that the conduct of most people in the body politic depends on the value indulgences and deprivations they have learned to expect to receive if they conform or nonconform to normative prescriptions (culture, class, interest group, and so on).

If deviations increase, the usual response of public policy-makers is to heighten the visible cost of deviation. At the same time, it is recognized that many individuals and groups are outside the reach of ordinary sanctions. For example, they do not share the presumably common culture as when they are reared in geographical or social isolation. Many defectives lack the capability required to attain culture norms; hence, ordinary penalties or rewards are without effect on their behavior.

It must also be noticed that the psychoanalytically oriented psychiatrist—who emphasizes the strength of the primary process—is usually called on in conjunction with attempts to obtain an exemption from ordinary sanctions. He is not alone in this, since the culturally oriented psychiatrist, social worker, or related specialist also tends to appear in public as part of a coalition in support of someone who is demanding exemption from, or modification of, ordinary sanctions. It is the witness for the rich defendant who is most likely to make the headlines, and it is notorious that the "battle of the psychiatrists" who testify on both sides of a controversy does not benefit the scientific credibility of the profession as a whole.

Perhaps it should be underlined that the decision-makers of the body politic are not provided with standards that can be "automatically" ap-

---

2. On the plight of the committed, see, for example, Edward DeGrazia (1955).

plied in difficult cases. This is, in fact, nothing new in the realm of public order. Scholarship has long provided data to support the conclusion that the "substantive" (or "content") principles that are supposed to guide the exercise of judgment are open to manifold interpretations. Hence, the principles of "procedure" followed by the decision-maker are relatively decisive. This means that the resolution of a conflict depends chiefly on the process by which one set of decision-makers rather than another is involved, and by which the focus of attention of the final decision-maker is drawn toward—or diverted from—various features of the context. In making various procedures available, public policy pursues many objectives. In general, the aim is to enable decision-makers to become sufficiently well acquainted with a set of situations to permit them to arrive at a more informed judgment than would otherwise be reached. This is the role of "hearing," "trial," and similar arrangements, which are designed to bring pertinent detail to the attention of decision-makers who have presumably been chosen by procedures that favor officials whose predispositions qualify them to act in the name of the community and in harmony with overriding objectives (Arens and Lasswell, 1961, pp. 198–236).

Quite recently a body of publicized opinion has begun to emerge within the field of psychiatry and law that criticizes the ideology of mental health in a more "liberal" frame of reference than usual. The demand is to reemphasize the scope of the individual's responsibility for his choice, and to advocate that community decision-makers refrain from interfering with these choices in the name of mental illness.[3] I suggest that this is one among many indications that the ideology of mental illness, which has been so widely extended in our society, will presently be restricted.

PROJECTING THE FUTURE

In estimating the future, I point to the principal tensions that divide the field of psychiatry at the present time. They are likely to be resolved in ways that diminish, rather than extend, the scope of "mental illness" and of "psychiatry."

At present, psychiatry is benefiting from the vogue of "mental health." "Community psychiatry" or "social psychiatry" are widely accepted terms. Although the scope of these conceptions is not yet standardized, the emerging pattern does at least include heavy reliance on out-patient therapy. Therapy by chemicals and by communication are both prominent, the latter in the form of group therapies that attempt to marshal collective pressure and to bring it to bear on deviating individuals. The result, I suspect, is closer to "suppressive therapy" than to the "insight therapy" cultivated by those who adhere to the orthodox procedures of

---

3. See the vigorous polemic by Thomas S. Szasz (1963).

psychoanalysis.[4] Group therapies are close to the strategies associated with social engineering; or, in general, to the manipulative methods of norm control that are utilized in nontherapeutic traditions. As group methods expand, the image of the psychiatrist will probably grow more dim, a development that will make it easier to merge manipulative strategies with the revivalistic tactics of religious institutions and with the admonitory or indoctrinational programs of other social sectors.

At first glance the use of chemicals might promise to keep the psychiatrist's image alive. However, the drug-dispensing role does not sharply differentiate the psychiatrist from the traditional doctor of medicine. The probable effect is to accentuate the cleavage between "somatically oriented" and "norm-managing" psychiatrists.

Programs in the name of community psychiatry are likely to come into more direct competition and conflict with programs that are justified in terms of "the new leisure" or "wider participation in education and culture." Social workers, social psychologists, lawyers, and others are implicated in these undertakings. It is probably safe to predict that social and behavioral scientists will gradually become less willing to follow the leadership of the psychiatric wing of medicine, especially when the norm-managing characteristics of community strategy become more evident.

The psychoanalysts, those who continue the orthodox practice of prolonged insight therapy, will, I foresee, remain in a distinctive though exposed position. Today they are being eroded from all sides by physicians, behavioral scientists, and others who complain of the cost of the psychoanalytic experience and who doubt that allegedly positive therapeutic results can be fully demonstrated. If psychoanalysts must defend themselves in the name of the research importance of their method or of its significance as a procedure of educational insight, it is virtually out of the question that public funds would be obtained on the scale necessary to enable everyone to be analyzed. If a psychoanalyst works an hour a day with each patient for a year, it is obvious that ten or twelve patients are all who can be treated in this period. In a psychiatric career extending over forty years, each analyst would deal intensively with less than 500 people. Obviously, the number can be increased if the intensiveness of the training is curtailed, but this reduces its distinctive potential.

For the most part, psychoanalysis will presumably continue to be an "elite experience" that, as a matter of cost, must be limited to those who look upon it favorably as an insight exposure of importance for psychiatrists and behavioral scientists. Budgetwise, we may expect it to be included among the costs of advanced training programs in these fields. Similarly, research on neurology and brain chemistry will probably be

---

4. I have benefited from discussion with my colleague, Robert Rubenstein; see also Robert Rubenstein and Harold D. Lasswell (1966, pp. 275–277).

budgeted as component elements of general research programs in physiology and medicine.

Our analysis points to the proposition that projects of cultural innovation are likely to be supported in the name of other than the ideology of mental health. If communities are to achieve their potential, it will be necessary to provide for the direct financing of community-leadership talent and programs. The ideology that most plausibly refers to such activities is "the cultivation of human resources," "cultural reconstruction," and the like.

POLICY IMPLICATIONS FOR MENTAL HEALTH

In the light of all that has gone before, what recommendations can be made about public policies toward mental health? I propose three general objectives, and end with a comment about shorter range manpower programs:

1. The long-range goal of public policy in reference to mental health is to vindicate the claim of every human being to achieve mental health.

2. As a means of achieving or approximating the goal, American society must have at its disposal a pool of manpower adequately motivated and skilled to identify mental illness and to provide the treatment required, while making sure that the sufferer does not have a seriously destructive impact on himself and others. In addition to treatment, manpower must be available for preventive measures. Treatment and preventive objectives imply the facilitation of scientific research to discover causal factors and to plan and appraise policies proposed or applied for both purposes.

3. Public policy requires a public whose members are educated to take note of symptoms of mental illness in themselves and others, and to seek expert assistance in verifying the condition and in coping with it. Such a policy calls for a stream of public information that serves as a reminder of mental health factors in society and assists in bringing their significance to the notice of the community. The policy also requires a corps of professionally trained persons who, in addition to their specialty, have received enough training in mental health matters to take the lead in acting as mediators between the mentally ill, the psychiatrist, and the community as a whole.

These continuing long-term objectives of public policy must be implemented by a series of programs at every level of American life—at national or subnational levels; employing the channels of government, of nonprofit private associations, and of private profit operations. At the governmental level, an appropriate balance must be sought among four types of function: (1) *enterprisory*, by which is meant responsibility for directly administered services (e.g., research, civil, or military treatment services) ; (2) *regulatory*, or the setting and application of standards for private activities (e.g., private hospitals) ; (3) *supervisory*, or the settlement of controversies concerning mental health initiated by private parties (as in suits for malpractice, or litigation over testimentary documents) ; (4) *sanctioning*, or the use of ordinary or corrective measures to deal with nonconformers to lawfully prescribed norms. In general, corrective sanctions are appropriate when the nonconformist is judged to be nonresponsible; that is, his deviation is an outcome of factors that are not perceived as standard for those who share the culture (as in the case, e.g., of organic mental defect, or emotional disturbances of exceptional severity in early development) .

I shall not undertake to formulate recommended criteria for delimiting the role of government further than to point out that in our body politic there is a continuing presumption in favor of private action, a presumption that can be overcome if net-value advantages can be shown in the event that preference is given to official over nonofficial channels.

If the policies adopted toward mental health by governmental or private organizations are to be influenced by available knowledge and expert judgment, available information must be made accessible in the policy-making and executing process of each organization. As indicated above, manpower programs need to take into account the need for well-informed intelligence and appraisal—intelligence for analysis and planning, and appraisal for estimates of the impact of past policy on subsequent events. Effective policy participation usually calls for some degree of promotional activity by political parties or pressure associations. The influence of such activities is reflected in prescriptions, in mental health legislation by public authority and in the bylaws of private operations. The policy process also calls for invocation (or the provisional application of prescriptions to concrete circumstances) , application (or final characterization of the situation) , and termination (or repeal of prescription, followed by the disposition of reasonable expectations built up when the norms were in effect, often in the form of compensation) .

Well-informed policy—whether on the part of federal, state, or local governments, or of private foundations, hospitals, and the like—obviously depends on a stream of intelligence about the aggregate role of mental illness and defect in society. It is not feasible to attempt to draw up a balance sheet that includes the positive role of "health"; "illness and defect" are easier to identify. Let us remind ourselves of what is involved in any comprehensive measurement (or rough estimate) of the impact of mental defect and illness in society. Consider a generalized model of the social process in terms of the shaping and sharing of value outcomes through institutions relatively specialized to each. Mental illness and defect are classified in this scheme as "negative well-being," since well-being is the label used to refer to interactions affecting safety, health, and comfort.

We have defined mental health as freedom from limitations in the central integrative process that lead to troubled and troublesome behavior. However, the "limitations" may be defined operationally; it is within range of present capability to arrive at provisional estimates of their effect on all eight of the value-institution activities referred to by our model. As the present symposium demonstrates, the best approximations to date refer to economic activities, or the shaping and sharing of wealth (e.g., loss of man-hours of production). Political impacts (power) are more complex. For instance, is national unity in crisis times consolidated or undermined by the agitational role or susceptibilities of the mentally ill? When we examine enlightenment activities—those concerned with acquiring or disseminating information—the task is to measure losses of capacity for scientific research, and to assess the role of the mentally disturbed in distorting the stream of information in public media. In the health field itself (well-being), we confront such perplexing questions as how mental disease contributes to or, on the contrary, retards other forms of pathology. I barely refer to other areas—education (skill), family relations (affection), social discrimination or recognition (respect), and ethical and religious norms and activities (rectitude).

Given the fragmentary character of present knowledge, it is obviously difficult to present an aggregate picture of cost in terms of *all* values; hence, it is not feasible to arrive at a realistic comparison of the economic and noneconomic costs, benefits, and risks of specific programs in mental health as distinguished from health in general, or from programs in other sectors.

Whatever present ambiguities there may be in aggregate appraisals of mental health, there is general acceptance of doing something positive to increase our knowledge and also to provide care and treatment for at least the most obvious sufferers. Owing to lack of agreement on the outer boundaries of the mental health sector, some of the programs presently supported in the name of mental health are likely to be viewed in the near future as less concerned with health policies than with the full utilization of human resources and with norm-changing activities (e.g., the discovery and cultivation of latent skill and initiatives for new subcultures—such as the use of drugs or diverse modes of sexual expression).

In order to lay a foundation for the many programs within or close to the mental health field, rather specific subprograms can be developed that depend on: (1) explicit definition of the phenomenon to be dealt with (e.g., mental defect); (2) appraisal of the impact of past (including current) policies designed to influence the phenomenon; (3) estimates of the manpower magnitudes required by alternative proposals of care, treatment, research, and preventive action. There are many indications of a trend toward the development of subprograms of this kind.

To recapitulate: The policy objectives presently defined in terms of the ideology of mental health are likely to recede. Operations closely related to somatic process will tend to merge with general physiology and medicine. Operations that rely on the manipulation of norms by the management of group projects are likely to merge with programs whose objectives are cultural reconstruction and the creative use of human resources. Well-informed manpower programs relevant to mental health, and mental health-related sectors, can be devised by selecting a package of specifiable subtargets.

REFERENCES

ARENS, R., and H. D. LASSWELL. 1961. *In defense of public order: the emerging field of sanction law.* New York: Columbia University Press.

DeGRAZIA, E. 1955. The distinction of being mad. *University of Chicago Law Review,* 22:339–355.

NAMENWIRTH, Z. J., and H. D. LASSWELL. Changing language in American party platforms: a computer analysis of political values. In press.

RUBENSTEIN, R., and H. D. LASSWELL. 1966. *The sharing of power in a psychiatric hospital.* New Haven: Yale University Press.

SHAKOW, D., and D. RAPAPORT. 1964. The influence of Freud on American psychology. *Psychological Issues,* 4 (1, Monograph No. 13).

SZASZ, T. S. 1963. *Law, liberty, and psychiatry: an inquiry into the social uses of mental health practices.* New York: Macmillan.

CHAPTER 4

Economic Aspects of
Mental Health Manpower

HERBERT E. KLARMAN

A PRECIS OF ECONOMIC CONCEPTS

THERE ARE THOSE WHO HOLD the view that the health and life of a person are so valuable that they are invaluable (beyond valuation) and that the economic calculus is irrelevant to this important area of concern. The economist's stance, by way of reply (even if only implied), is that outside the Garden of Eden, following the fall, resources are scarce, so that choices must constantly be made among competing goals and programs. Moreover, whatever society's goals may be, it makes sense to try to attain them at the lowest possible cost through the appropriate combination of personnel, equipment, and supplies.

Stated concisely, the central problem of economics is that resources are scarce relative to the many wants that people have. All social and private goals cannot be pursued simultaneously, and even an affluent society is bound to choose between what it will and will not do at a given time. In a world with full employment, the cost of undertaking program A is the foregoing of program B (Stigler, 1952, p. 2).

I was most fortunate in the choice of my discussant, Professor Mary Jean Bowman. Her constructive comments have enabled me to effect many improvements in the paper. I regret my inability to incorporate all of her suggestions.

In considering policies for mental health manpower, it seems axiomatic that the recruitment, training, and employment of personnel can be justified only by the value of the services (care, counseling, teaching, or research) that they perform. Few economists would justify the filling of particular jobs by the contribution made to the reduction of unemployment (Klarman, 1965a, p. 55). Maintaining full employment or promoting a higher rate of economic growth is regarded by most economists as the responsibility of the fiscal and monetary authorities—individuals and institutions who determine the amount of taxes levied, the volume of government expenditures, the amount of money in circulation, and the rate of interest.

It is recognized, of course, that available personnel limit the scope of programs today and in the near future. However, personnel "shortages" should not be treated as if they precluded the mounting of programs in the long run and do not justify failure to pursue them. Rather, the determining criteria for expanding or contracting programs are costs and benefits, with costs measured appropriately to reflect scarcities in personnel.

The formal criterion for the optimum size of program is equality between marginal (differential or incremental) costs and marginal benefits. (The marginal cost of producing A is the total cost of producing $n + 1$ units minus the total cost of producing n units.) Rarely is the problem that of choosing between all or nothing; rather, it is that of more or less.

When marginal benefits exceed marginal costs, it is appropriate to expand a program. Conversely, a program should be contracted when marginal benefits fall short of marginal costs. (In case of the business firm, substitute "revenue" for "benefits.")

At least by intention all benefits and all costs are counted. It is likely to prove mischievous to disregard certain benefits—to treat them as if they were worth zero—just because it is difficult to measure them. It is certainly erroneous to disregard certain costs because they are incurred by some other level of government, agency, or group of persons.

The link between costs and benefits is a technological datum to the economist. To have meaning in the real world, however, it must be validated. There is no point in arguing over the adoption of a program with effectiveness unknown, unless steps are taken to acquire the necessary information.

APPROACHES TO HEALTH MANPOWER

Before proceeding to suggest a conceptual scheme for looking at the mental health manpower problem, in light of the propositions briefly outlined in the preceding section, I shall discuss the approaches to health manpower currently in vogue. The presentation of method, combined with a critique, will serve to throw light on what we are now doing, indicate where we fall short, and expose opportunities for useful borrowing.

By now a considerable body of literature exists on planning for health manpower. Most of it deals with physicians and nurses as independent categories.

In this literature two general sets of approaches are discernible. The first belongs to public health officials and planners, who measure requirements for and availabilities of personnel separately. They subtract one from the other and arrive at a determination of shortage or surplus for a particular category of personnel.

The other approach belongs to economists, who emphasize the earnings of an occupation. From trends in earnings they tend to draw inferences about shortage or surplus, usually in approximate fashion.

Thus, public health planners measure *gross* requirements for personnel, while economists deal with *net additional* requirements, which may be negative or positive.

Public Health Approaches

In the publications of health planners, still another dichotomy is discernible: measuring personnel requirements (1) according to a population's need for services and (2) on the basis of personnel-to-population ratios.

Need. The need approach was developed and applied by Lee and Jones (1933) in their classic monograph for the Committee on the Costs of Medical Care. The procedure is quite systematic: ascertain the frequency of occurrence of injuries and diseases in a population; translate the frequencies into requirements for services; and, in turn, convert services into manpower.

The appeal of this method lies in its presumed scientific objectivity. Need is held to have been determined by professional, expert opinion. The appeal gains support from the widespread consensus in this country that medical need, rather than financial ability to pay for services, should govern access to health services.

Nevertheless, this method has certain weaknesses. Translating data on disease, when known, into requirements for services is not so simple a task. By approaching the problem *de novo*, and strictly from a technical, medical standpoint, it is easy to neglect the effects of culture, social class, and economic means on the use of health services. After all, not every measure that is known for diagnosing and treating illness is to be applied under any circumstances, and there must be some nontechnical bases for selecting the measures that will be applied.

Even the conversion of requirements for services into requirements for personnel is fraught with difficulties. One, how much time on the average to allow for a service? There are differences between general practitioners and internists, by geographic area and by customary usage. Two, how long should a physician work? The average physician works long hours—nearly sixty hours a week—but probably no longer than some other professionals. Three, what fraction of the work week should be spent on seeing patients, in contrast to attendance at professional meetings, reading the literature, teaching, research, participation in planning health services, etc?

Finally, as a matter of public policy, it appears to me unwise to provide resources at a specified, measured level unless need can be converted promptly into demand (1) through underwriting appropriate financial arrangements and (2) by persuading people to recognize and accept— that is, to seek—the services they are said to need. The last proviso is frequently overlooked and public education is not undertaken.

Resources would be wasted through disuse, except in circumstances when an increase in supply is conducive to an increase in demand. On this point I am inclined to the view that despite conflicting evidence, the phenomenon seems quite real in the general hospital field under conditions of widespread prepayment (Roemer, 1961; Rosenthal, 1964, pp. 55–62). The explanatory factors are not yet known, however. The relative importance of the low elasticity of demand (the relative unresponsiveness of the quantity demanded to a change in price), the social and cultural aspects of changing standards and expectations of hospital use, and the possible operation of a rationing scheme in the presence of a long waiting line is still to be determined.

From a broader, more philosophical, standpoint, the need approach implies an absolute priority for the health field over other economic sectors in commanding specified types and amounts of resources. One of the lessons economics teaches, Clark (1949, p. 54) has well said, is that single aims carry a very high price.

Personnel-to-population ratios. For each category of personnel, this approach carries two major variants. The first, developed through the 1930's in the U.S. Public Health Service, brings all geographic areas below some selected standard ratio (derived from the array of ratios for all areas) up to that standard, without changing anything in the areas that exceed it. The standard selected may be the arithmetic average, median, third quartile, ninetieth percentile, etc. (Mountin, Pennell, and Berger, 1949).

The second variant was developed during World War II as an offshoot of Selective Service policy in drafting physicians, dentists, and nurses. This variant applies the existing personnel-to-population ratio to the population projected for the future, and, in addition, usually takes into account certain requirements that are currently unmet or are visibly emerging. An example of this approach is the well-known Bane Commission report (1959) on physicians.

Sometimes both variants of the personnel-to-population ratio approach are employed in the same report, with the lower estimate of requirements offered as the more conservative one (National Commission, 1967). The appeal of the personnel-to-population approach in either variant is obvious; it is a simple procedure, dependent on a few statistics that are usually available, which permits precise numerical calculations.

The objections to this approach have been voiced by economists from time to time. The following formulation reflects a broad consensus, I believe.

The first variant of the personnel-to-population ratio approach— bringing all areas below a certain standard up to it, leaving untouched the areas that exceed the standard—is bound to lead to the finding that a shortage exists. The amount of shortage depends on the ratio selected as the standard. The standard is, in turn, a function of the point on the array that is chosen and also of the degree of variation in personnel-to-population ratios that exists among areas. Given the method, it would be surprising if a shortage were not always calculated (Dickinson, 1950). Indeed, it is conceivable that if successful action were taken to eliminate today's shortage, as indicated by this method, and if the size of geographic variation increased as the personnel-to-population ratios rose, an even larger numerical shortage might be calculated in the future.

Under the second variant, there is an assumption, untested, that the current situation is satisfactory. This method always deals with the future, with population growth signifying an increased requirement for health personnel. The anticipated increase in supply may or may not prove to be adequate to meet the higher requirement.

Two assumptions are made on the requirements side. Explicit is a projection of the population, as noted above, which not infrequently proves to be erroneous. Implied is a stable balance between the factors governing per capita use of services (the income of the population, relative prices of goods and services, and consumer tastes or preferences, which incorporate the demographic and social characteristics of the population) on the one hand, and those governing the average productivity of health personnel (the state of technology, availability of substitute factors of production and their relative prices, and economies associated with the scale of operation) on the other.

Economists' Approaches

Most economists—by no means all—focus on income. Harris (1964) has said, "I know of no more relevant index of shortage of doctors than the great rise of incomes of physicians" (p. 147). It is recognized, of course, that incomes tend to fluctuate from year to year. The economist draws inferences from incomes that are persistently high or low.

Two different approaches are employed under this heading, and considerable controversy exists between their proponents.

One approach is to compare the rate of change in income for the occupation under study with the rate of change in income for other occupations. According to Blank and Stigler (1957), if the relative income of the former occupation rises, a shortage exists.

This approach has been criticized on several grounds (Hansen, 1964; Weiss, 1966; Yett, 1968). There is the assumption of an optimum allocation of workers among occupations in some base year. At any rate, it is not possible to discern when the shortage in a particular occupation began (and, obversely, when a surplus began elsewhere). As the relative income of an occupation rises, the particular shortage and surpluses elsewhere may indeed be diminishing, as market forces work out the processes of adjustment over time. Finally, perhaps most important, changing costs of entry into an occupation are neglected, including income foregone during training. (Although universally accepted by economists, this last item is sometimes regarded outside the profession as novel in the sense of being odd [Gross, 1967, p. 429].) If an occupation's training period is lengthened, annual income may be expected to rise in offset.

A modification of the Blank-Stigler approach by Rayack (1964) infers a shortage only when an attempt is made to substitute less costly services for more costly ones in the face of a rise in relative income. The difficulty here, it seems to me, is that the maximum in cost effectiveness always calls for such substitution in an effort to produce a given output at the lowest possible cost.

The other approach employed by economists is to calculate the internal rate of return that equates the present (capital) value of the expected earnings of an occupation to the present value of its costs and then to compare this rate of return with those of other occupations today and in the past. This method was applied to two health professions by Hansen (1964), who adapted it from the classic study of the present value of earnings of the independent professions conducted by Friedman and Kuznets (1945).

The internal rate-of-return method is intellectually satisfying. Although the criterion is not strictly correct, it usually suffices for practical purposes (Borland and Yett, 1966; Hansen, 1967). However, its assumptions for the health field should be spelled out and appraised.

Where freedom of choice of occupation exists, the earnings of an occupation are assumed to reflect society's valuation of its services. The presence of external or spillover effects of services (on persons other than the direct purchasers or consumers of services) is neglected. Although I do not regard this to be an important factor for most personal health services (with the exception of communicable diseases), it may loom large for mental health services. If so, earnings would represent an underestimate of the true value of such services to society (Holtmann, 1965) .

Important is the method's implicit assumption that the proper aim of public policy is to achieve the position of competitive equilibrium, under which the allocation of resources is deemed to be the most efficient possible (given the distribution of income and, as above, abstracting from spillover effects) . There are expressed disagreements with this goal for physicians, however, which point in opposite directions. On the one hand, some economists would like to see a surplus of physicians, as assurance of access to one when needed (Holtmann, 1965; Rayack, 1965) . Some, on the other hand, favor a taut supply, on the ground that physicians are able to generate a demand for their services when hard-pressed financially (Ginzberg, 1966b) . A serious risk of overdoctoring arises, which can do harm. The import of this latter point of view is that at some levels of physician income, the demand for and supply of their services are no longer independent.

This method further assumes that the relationship of the nonpecuniary returns of an occupation—satisfaction, prestige, responsibility, autonomy —to its financial returns remains unchanged over time. Economists have long recognized that the operative tendency in the market, where mobility exists, is to equalize the total returns from occupations—pecuniary plus nonpecuniary, not just pecuniary (Boulding, 1954) . If the prestige of an occupation changes, a compensatory increase or decrease in financial returns may be indicated. If the prestige of public and private psychiatrists differs, pecuniary offsets may be required. If social security is adopted and spreads through the economy, the edge formerly enjoyed by the public sector in affording stable employment and retirement pensions disappears, and again financial inducements must be substituted.

Recent Studies by Economists

Fein (1967) has projected physician requirements on the basis of use of services by various socioeconomic and demographic components of the population. This method starts from the realistic base of actual use and avoids the thicket of allocating a practitioner's work week between patient care and other professional activities. The study is subject to two types of criticism. No appraisal is attempted of prevailing patterns of use —that is, whether more or less use would be beneficial relative to cost. This is a formidable task, of course. On the supply side, too little is known about the effects on the productivity of physicians of differences in form of medical-care organization and of substitution among categories of personnel. Consequently, speculation and close reasoning take the place of the missing facts.

Another basis for measuring personnel requirements is the use of services by a defined population with specified characteristics (Klarman, 1951) , which was recently employed by the staff of the Canadian Royal

Commission on Health Services (Judek, 1964). A major difficulty in calculations, not yet solved, is to ascertain the true numerator (services) and denominator (population) for both the population served and the personnel rendering the services. Assumptions are that under the prepaid group-practice arrangement, the staffing permits the provision of all services deemed desirable from a professional standpoint (and also sought by subscribers) (Reder, 1967), and that the professional criteria are consistent with judgments that would be made on cost-benefit grounds (broadly interpreted to include all costs and all benefits, whatever their distance may be from pricing by the market). It is also necessary to posit a financial underwriting of at least the specified level of care.

Weiss (1966) has employed a third approach, which might be used in conjunction with the second. He focused on the type of service used, not on occupational category. Drawing on Young's work in the Survey of Dentistry (1961), he concluded that with support by auxiliary personnel, dentists can increase the output of dental services. It is only fair to note that so far this approach has performed much more successfully in analyzing dental care than nursing care.

Weiss' approach, with its emphasis on the possibilities of substituting one type of personnel (less costly) for another (more costly) in producing a given set of services, possesses inherent appeal for economists.

DISTINCTIVE ECONOMIC CHARACTERISTICS OF MENTAL HEALTH SERVICES

A pervasive note in the preceding discussion and critique of the public health and economists' approaches to health manpower planning is the need to appraise whether the volume of services actually rendered is appropriate—that is, whether an increase or reduction from present levels may not be indicated. To make the point explicit, the suggestion is that cost-benefit analysis be applied, the term being used broadly to denote a systematic and comprehensive way of looking at programs.

A prior question is in order: Why cost-benefit analysis? This is a method of analyzing proposed public expenditures when the market economy does not provide reliable guidance through prices. The literature on the economics of health contains several treatments of the distinguishing economic characteristics of health services, including those that warrant public intervention (Arrow, 1963; Klarman, 1965a, pp. 47–56; Mushkin, 1964; Weisbrod, 1961, pp. 16–27). Here it is proposed to focus on the special characteristics of mental health services.

Care of mental illness may be said to partake of some of the characteristics of external or spillover effects. Classic examples of external effects in the health field are afforded by communicable diseases. Here a vaccination serves to protect not only its recipient against a disease but also his family, friends, and neighbors. The value of the vaccination to the community is greater than its value to the individual recipient. Since the price system tends to reflect the values placed on a service by those directly involved in the transaction, the presence of externalities indicates the likelihood of undervaluation and raises the question of whether public intervention may not be in order.

Mental illnesses are not communicable, certainly not in any strict sense. There are those, however, who see many forms of mental illness as a function of the socioeconomic environment and adverse changes in it (Gans, 1967). Gains in the economy improve the environment and reduce stress. This theory is far from proved; Mishler and Scotch (1965, p. 272) observe that the notion that downward mobility, with its attendant stress, leads to schizophrenia can be found only in the layman's theory of mental illness.

However, other forms of externality have long been recognized in the treatment of patients with psychosis. The major emphasis given to involuntary confinement in the past reflects only in part the ineffectiveness of treatment. It also reflects the weight given to protecting the rest of the community.

With confinement and isolation of the patient in an institution removed from centers of population goes the "stigma" of having mental illness. The cost of stigma is high for those who have had such illness, even if cured, and for their families (Klarman, 1965c). Here is a clear instance when, from an economic standpoint, prevention is preferable to cure, if prevention is available even at somewhat higher cost. The cost of stigma may have been reduced somewhat by the shift in the location of psychiatric treatment toward community facilities and by the enhanced effectiveness of treatment, including its shorter duration.

It is widely recognized that patients are not expert in judging the quality of health services, with the possible exception of the amenities of care. In the presence of consumer ignorance, society deems it necessary to take steps to protect buyers, and in the health field the prime measure is the tradition of professional responsibility, supported by state licensure. As previously noted in the discussion of the internal rate-of-return approach, there may be dangers in putting exclusive reliance on the professional integrity of physicians without regard for other incentives that may be operative.

What is not so generally recognized is that sometimes the providers of services are ignorant, too. Physicians do not always know what the end results of therapies are. In that case, a profession tends to rely for its judgments of the quality of care on the conformity of process to the best prevailing practices (Zubin, 1964). In view of the large public stake in the mental health field, and apart from the large public interest in medical research as such, it is imperative to correct the existing gap in knowledge of the end results achieved by mental health services.

Combined with the presence of externalities, prolonged duration of treatment and high cost have entailed substantial public financing of mental illness treatment. As long as the primary facility was the large mental hospital, the state was by far the predominant source of funds. Local governments have been slow to develop other types of mental care facilities, owing to their understandable reluctance to relieve the states of this financial responsibility. Recent federal legislation has both generated federal subsidies for community mental health centers and accentuated the trend toward separating the financing of services by government from the production of such services. There is some suggestive evidence that where the financial supporter of a service also owns and operates the facility, the criteria of eligibility to receive the service are likely to be more liberal than under conditions of purchase.

In private psychiatric practice there is almost exclusive reliance on private financing, mostly out of pocket and outside the scope of voluntary health insurance. The appropriate role of health insurance in paying for the care of mental illness is a subject of controversy (Bamberger, 1965; Glasser, 1965). Some of the disagreements revolve about the technical devices employed to control the use of services.

Health insurance plans are likely to rely on financial deterrents to the use of psychiatric services, while governmental programs are more likely to rely on professional or organizational controls. Financial devices in the form of deductibles and coinsurance are of uncertain effectiveness as deterrents for most health services, but are perhaps powerful in the mental health field, where major medical insurance plans have been steadily increasing their size. This power cannot, of course, be divorced from the level of the deterrents.

It may be argued that not only does health insurance reduce the price of the service at the time it is used, thereby increasing the amount of services demanded, but the subscriber may feel he has earned the right to use the service, having paid for it through his premium. In the case of mental illness the prospect of stigma would, however, weaken this tendency.

In addition, the controversy on the role of health insurance reflects the uncertainty and ignorance concerning the effects of various regimes of treatment. Often insurance policies for mental illness with different benefits apply to socioeconomic groups with different expectations on their part as to mode of treatment and probable outcome, and with different degrees of access to various types of facilities and personnel, who in turn apply to them different criteria for diagnosis and treatment (Hollingshead, 1960).

The extent to which sources of funds for the care of mental illness are diversified is thus important for the choice of treatment modalities. It also affects the total amount spent for care. Elsewhere (Klarman, 1965a,

p. 41), I have observed that the amount spent on health services is likely to be greater when two or more sources of financing are operative, namely because at a given time different sources enjoy different capabilities for raising and spending money. Only in the event that gaps in service become less visible in the presence of diverse sources of financing, and, therefore, more tolerable, is the amount of expenditures likely to be smaller than under a single source of financing.

OBJECTIVES AND PRIORITIES OF EXPENDITURE

In the preceding section I have endeavored to demonstrate the public interest in the provision of mental health services. In turn, this demonstration justifies the application of the cost-benefit approach.

Before outlining the technical elements of the cost-benefit calculation, I shall discuss two topics of more general interest. The first pertains to health expenditures for growth or for consumer satisfaction. The point of this discussion is that the output of programs oriented toward consumer satisfaction is much more difficult to measure, so that often the economist's role is likely to be that of the cost-effectiveness analyst, who accepts the program goals determined through the political process.

The second topic deals with the nature of priorities among programs, with particular emphasis on the shifts that may be expected to accompany progress.

Growth vs. Consumption

A frequent distinction made is that between expenditures for health services as an "investment" in future production or in the potential saving of resources employed in the health field and expenditures for purchasing consumer satisfaction.

The first type of expenditure, which promotes economic growth, is subject to the ordinary and well-known criteria of profit and loss calculation. If the private market is operative, no more need be said; in general, profits will tend to be maximized or losses minimized.

If the market is not fully operative, the calculation is complicated by the need to estimate imputed prices and to adopt one or more social discount (interest) rates for calculating the present value of a future stream of services, as well as by the opportunity to take account of external effects, as previously noted. (All economic terms that are not defined here are explained in the next section.)

Expenditures for consumer satisfaction could also be handled simply if the private market were fully operative. The willingness of consumers to buy various quantities of goods at alternative prices reflects their incomes (both level and distribution by size; the latter may be changed by public policy), tastes or preferences, and the prices of the goods in question relative to those of other goods closely related in use as substitutes or complements. Actual use will be determined by the interaction of demand and supply, with the latter closely related to a proper measure of cost.

When the market for consumer goods is not operative or not fully operative, as in mental health services, tastes or preferences must be expressed through the mediation of the political process. There is no unique—objective, uniform, and stable—way for a community to choose between a school and a psychiatric service in a general hospital (Burkhead, 1956, pp. 250–251).

In actuality, the two types of expenditure—economic growth and consumption—are likely to be incurred at the same time and are not readily disentangled. Perhaps the best that can be done in practice is to attribute to a given program its predominant weight, that of a growth expenditure or a consumption expenditure, and to treat it accordingly. It is certainly misleading to assume a uniform ratio of consumption-to-growth benefits for all health programs, as is sometimes done for convenience (Weisbrod, 1961, pp. 95–98).

The distinction between expenditures for growth and for consumer satisfaction has certain implications. If the results of a program are of the growth type, they will increase total Gross National Product (GNP) directly by raising output, or increase the segment of GNP that represents nonmental health expenditures by releasing resources from mental health services. If the results are of a consumption nature, a portion of the GNP must be allocated to it (Lees, 1960). The latter competes with other current consumption expenditures; and, if the expenditures for mental health services are large enough, the question arises whether they can be afforded under existing circumstances.

In sum, it is sometimes easier for a society to proceed directly with growth types of expenditure, while consumption types of expenditure wait, pending the growth of GNP. I suspect, however, that this distinction is much more relevant to a poor, developing nation than to one developed and relatively affluent, like ours.

Another implication of the distinction is probably more important in our society. Benefits from growth types of expenditure tend to be measurable in terms of a common denominator, the dollar. Benefits from consumption types of expenditure may be difficult to measure objectively. Ultimately, the answer concerning the latter is given by tastes or preferences, the values held by the members of society at a given time.

With respect to expenditures for consumption, the investigator has three options. He can persist in attempting to measure what is so difficult to measure, by inferring values from society's actions in various matters. He can abandon the search for measurement of the benefits of alternative programs, and simply adopt a given bundle of benefits as the settled goal of policy, which may be pursued through alternative ways. In that case each program will be costed, as in cost effectiveness (Klarman, Francis, and Rosenthal, 1968). He may limit himself to listing all the expected consequences of a program, and try to attach to some a magnitude of rank or scale, not quantity (Rothenberg, 1965).

Priorities

When measurement of all costs and all benefits is possible, priorities among programs can be derived from the levels and shapes of the respective cost and benefit functions, which are reflected in the present value of the future streams of benefits and costs. If a program expands appreciably, its costs are likely to rise, as resources that are less well adapted to the purpose at hand are recruited and prices of resources rise in order to induce their transfer. The extent to which costs rise will depend in part on the rate at which a program is expanded.

The benefits of a program may decline, owing to the increasing difficulties of case-finding or the intractability of some persons in treatment. If so, the program will lose its priority, giving ground to another program still in its early phase and not yet subject to rising cost or declining benefits.

The basic point is that priorities for programs are not absolute, because few cost and benefit functions are likely to be constant. The objective is to derive equal benefits from the last dollar spent on every program that is undertaken (Weisbrod, 1961).

Nor can it be said that preventive programs always enjoy priority over treatment programs. Clearly, preventive measures are superior to curative measures of equal cost when they are equally efficacious; conceivably, the former may be superior even when they are more costly, the reason being that successful prevention avoids the pain, grief, and discomfort associated with illness and avoids an increase in susceptibility to other illnesses. With respect to mental illness, successful prevention also avoids the stigma of a person's having had the disease.

Prevention cannot be superior to treatment, however, when effective preventive measures are not known, while curative or ameliorative measures are known and can be applied.

ELEMENTS OF COST-BENEFIT CALCULATION

Reference has been made to the calculation of costs and benefits. In formal terms, and subject to our ability to measure all the elements, the aim is to measure the difference between the sum of all benefits and total costs, each expressed as the present value of its expected future streams, after discounting (Prest and Turvey, 1965).

Benefits are frequently measured by costs (Fein, 1958, pp. 3–5; Weisbrod, 1961, p. 5), thereby causing confusion. Benefits are expected costs that will be averted through the implementation of a program. In the health field, benefits are usually classified in three categories: (1) tangible direct—savings in the use of health resources; (2) tangible indirect —earnings of persons saved from death or disability; and (3) intangible health benefits—pleasure over well-being, the absence of grief or pain, etc. The two sets of tangible benefits may be equated with the growth types of expenditure in the preceding section, and intangible benefits with consumption types of expenditure.

Costs are projected expenditures over time, as in a budget, plus items that are not reflected in the budget, such as earnings foregone during training. Other items of cost may be expenditures by patients for travel, as well as the values attached to travel time and waiting time.

Discounting

Why apply discounting? We are all aware that to have a dollar today that we do not own, we must borrow at interest. Similarly, if we agree to forego the present use of money and lend it, we expect to receive interest. Interest payment is required by time preference (preference for the present over the future) and is made possible in large part by the productivity of capital. To allocate resources efficiently between present and future uses, discounting is essential even when capital is not privately owned.

It is perhaps more problematical whether discounting should apply to consumption benefits (Feldstein, 1966), but I believe that it does. Here, too, time preference is involved, in the sense that pleasure, pain, grief, or discomfort that accrues over time may appear more dim in the distant future, and has a reduced probability of occurrence for an individual, due to ultimate death. The element of the productivity of capital is lacking, however.

Economists accept the necessity of discounting almost as a truism for making disparate future streams of costs or benefits commensurate. Public health planners sometimes have difficulty in accepting it (Stickle, 1965), apparently, because they see it as an indication of the pervasiveness of the dollar sign in areas previously considered sacred and beyond (above) pecuniary valuation. I agree that a man's livelihood should not be confused with the value of his life (Schilling, 1966) ; the technical procedure of discounting—a way of allowing for futurity—is the wrong target, however.

Economists do not agree on the proper level of the discount rate (Rothenberg, 1967, pp. 107–110). Some would employ the market rate of interest, after adjustment for taxes and degrees of uncertainty. Private and collective estimates of time preferences are likely to diverge, because the individual tends to have a shorter time horizon than society. Moreover, time preference may vary by social class, with the upper classes more willing to postpone gratification (Simmons, 1958, p. 26). The public interest may thus require varying degrees of intervention, apart from differences in the ability of groups to pay for mental health services.

Economists usually prepare alternative estimates of the present value of costs and benefits, depending on the discount rate. Another reason advanced for the dual rate procedure is that the discount rate represents a judgment on the relative importance of successive generations, a judgment on which opinions may differ. As life expectancy lengthens, this problem diminishes somewhat as the present generation's time horizon is extended.

The level of the discount rate has a strong effect on the size of the present value if the time period considered is long, with a high rate reducing the present value and conversely. The choice of discount rates becomes a serious problem in the evaluation of programs for patients with chronic diseases.

The rate most frequently appearing in the literature—the mode—is 6 per cent, which is also intermediate in the range of rates that have been employed (Klarman, 1965b).

Tangible Direct Benefits

The measurement of the value of tangible direct benefits is practicable when benefits are known. In this area the economist emphasizes the marginal cost to be averted, both because this is the relevant cost for decision-making and because the other type of cost, average cost, cannot be calculated without ambiguity when several goods are produced jointly (McKean, 1958, pp. 44–45).

Owing to the simultaneous presence of several diseases, however, there is a tendency to overstate the benefits accruing from the implementation of a given health services program (Mushkin, 1962). If every person with disease had only one, it would be appropriate to add the benefits of reducing the effects of disease A and disease B. When a person has two or more diseases at the same time, reducing or even eliminating one still leaves him with one or more diseases, which can also contribute to the continuance of economic losses. If the treatment for two diseases is the same, the problem posed here is removed. When treatment for the diseases simultaneously present differs, and prognoses vary, the failure to consider the second disease results in an overstatement of the potential economic benefits. The risk of overstating potential benefits is greatest when the several diseases are interdependent in origin, as they often are in families with multiple problems. Syphilis, for example, may be associated with tuberculosis and alcoholism (Klarman, 1965c).

Another possible source of overstatement is the counting of all institutional expenditures, including room and board, in the cost of medical care. This is especially true in long-term illness, when the patient no longer maintains a home.

Tangible Indirect Benefits

Procedures for valuing tangible indirect benefits have evolved rapidly in recent years, to the point that considerable agreement exists on the treatment of various elements of the calculation. A fairly routine procedure is approaching adoption (Rice, 1966). The economic contribution of labor is measured by earnings, not by income (earnings plus revenue from property). The expected value of earning is the arthmetic mean, not the median. The participation rate in the labor force is taken as that prevailing for the same sex and age (and perhaps also race and education) group. Full employment (4 per cent unemployment) is assumed, having been achieved presumably through appropriate fiscal and monetary policies.

The assumption of full employment is vulnerable on the ground that persons who have been mentally ill and rehabilitated do not usually enjoy equal job opportunities with those who have escaped such illness.

There is still disagreement on the treatment of housewives' services and consumption. Increasingly, it is accepted that housewives' services must be measured somehow, because to exclude them is to favor programs in which male beneficiaries predominate. The prevailing measure of value is on the conservative side, taken at the level of earnings of a full-time maid. Alternative procedures are in terms of refined estimates of what it takes to replace the housewife at home, such as Weisbrod's (1961, pp. 114–119), or what it takes to attract her into the labor market (including earnings adjusted for taxes and the extra expenses of going to work).

How to treat consumption is the same question as, Should the earnings of program beneficiaries be taken gross or net? In this country, more and more economists tend *not* to deduct consumption. The reasoning is that man is not a machine, and consumption is the ultimate goal of economic activity (Fein, 1958, pp. 18–20). Society's concern is with total output, of which consumption is the major component (Mushkin and Collings, 1959).

Intangible Benefits

Consumption benefits (or intangible benefits) are the third category of potential benefits. These are still untractable to measurement, although a number of devices have been employed and more approaches proposed. Among them are applications from insurance and game theory— what people would be willing to pay for specified reduction in the probability of occurrence; expenditures incurred for analogous diseases at old age, when tangible economic benefits can no longer be realized (except perhaps in managing property and investments); jury verdicts in the case of accidents and occupational illness (presumably after expected lifetime earnings are removed); the implications for health of past decisions on public expenditures to eliminate highway crossings at grade; and the sheer listing of certain known consequences, without economic valuation, such as a reduction in the incidence of orphanhood resulting from a reduction of mortality in the middle years (Klarman, 1965b; Mushkin, 1962).

By and large, the literature on health economics tends to neglect intangible benefits. The failure to take them into account is either not noted or appears in a footnote as a mild qualification of quantified results. My own work in the field of syphilis control indicates that the analogous-diseases approach is versatile and capable of yielding numerical results that are independent of the other components of the cost-benefit calculation (Klarman, 1965c, pp. 400, 403).

In a full-fledged cost-benefit analysis, neglect of a major element of the calculation is not only a serious oversight; it may lead to a distortion of priorities among alternative programs. From a practical standpoint, it may be the better part of wisdom under these circumstances to retreat to cost-effectiveness analysis, under which the goals sought are decided on other grounds, with the economic analysis confined to ascertaining the best mix of inputs for achieving the stated goals (Klarman, Francis, and Rosenthal, 1968).

Transfer Payments

I would feel neglectful of my duty as an economist if I refrained from mentioning such frequently listed benefits of health service programs as income taxes collected on subsequent earnings or the termination of public assistance grants. Most economists regard these items as transfer payments—representing a shift in the command over resources—and not a cost averted in the sense of entailing the use of resources. I believe that to treat changes in transfer payments as changes in economic benefits is to engage in double or triple counting of true benefits.

It is realistic to recognize that government expenditures, as in the field of mental illness, may flow from different coffers. When one level of government incurs an expenditure while another collects income taxes from the earnings of the program's beneficiaries or reduces its expenditures for relief, problems arise in the distribution of financial ability to pay that are additional to, and separate from, considerations of economic efficiency. Public policy is as much concerned with the former as with the latter.

EVALUATION IN MENTAL HEALTH

In evaluating the costs and benefits of programs, it is presumed that some causal link exists between inputs (costs) and outputs (benefits). There is scarcely any point to the calculation if no such link exists—that is, if we do not know how to affect the mortality or morbidity from a given disease or how to improve the health status of persons who receive care. In the absence of data on the outcome of programs, the problem of economic valuation disappears (Musgrave, 1965, pp. 38–39).

Reasons for Shortcomings

To establish this link in the mental health field may be difficult, as demonstrated by a recent study that compares costs in three psychiatric facilities. McCaffree (1967) has found short-term, intensive care to be more economical than long-term care, with the greatest difference occurring in the indirect tangible benefits. The study's underlying assumption is that the patients cared for in the three settings do not differ by diagnosis or prognosis in the absence of treatment. McCaffree (1966) believes that the economist can make no other reasonable supposition, when he has no information to the contrary from clinicians or epidemiologists.

Unfortunately, it is not a rarity for the underlying technological data that the economist requires to be lacking or suspect. Under the circumstances, I can envisage three choices open to the economist.

One choice in calculating the benefits of a program is to assume total eradication of the disease in question—that is, count the entire current cost as the potential benefit. I believe that this approach is unrealistic and conducive to faulty policy decisions for several reasons. A large-scale program is not merely a small-scale program expanded in proportion, because the structure of costs may differ and also the structure of benefits; this point has been made in the discussion of priorities. The side effects of large programs may be so much greater than for small programs that they can no longer be disregarded.

Another choice is to posit a reduction of one-tenth or one-fourth or one-half in the size of the existing problem or to assume a reduction in the nationwide level to a better, lower level prevailing in one of its regions. These assumptions are less mischievous in practice but may be misleading if they help create the impression that we know how to achieve the stated reduction.

The third, and, in my opinion, preferred choice is to try to ascertain what it is now feasible to accomplish through the provision of health services (Paul, 1967; Zubin, 1964). Under existing knowledge, what difference would an expansion or contraction of a particular program make? In addition, what are the especially promising prospects for medical research? What opportunities confront us in the more widespread application of accepted knowledge?

The economist should request of the epidemiologist clear definitions of outcome attributable to the provision of health services. The economist bases his calculations on specific events, such as death, disability, employment, episodes of illness, and use of health services. Each event has a place on the calendar and some have additional dimensions, such as duration and intensity. Ideally, such data should extend as close as possible to the individual's entire lifetime (Klarman, 1965b).

Information of this type is frequently lacking. Elsewhere (Klarman, 1965b), I have listed some reasons for this. Briefly, physicians may disagree on both diagnosis and prognosis, because medicine is not an exact science; the best data would come from longitudinal studies, which are not common in our society; the presence of asymptomatic disease may impair the conclusions drawn from the observation of control groups; the possibility of disease induced by medical care itself leads to a requirement for more field studies of normal populations, which are far more costly to perform than clinical studies of hospitalized patients; and populations differ in the simultaneous presence and detection of multiple diseases.

It should be noted, too, that economists have seldom specified the types of data required to perform cost-benefit calculations. Indeed, many economists tend to avoid involvement in questions of the underlying technology and institutional aspects of medical care, and prefer to regard the medical profession's statements on personnel requirements as expressions of scientific judgments (Somers and Somers, 1967, pp. 36–37). In recent years, however, an increasing number of economists working in the health field have come to realize that the quality of their analyses cannot transcend the validity of the underlying data. Accordingly, they have begun to judge the data with which they work, and to seek improvement (Fuchs, 1966; Klarman, 1965c).

Epidemiologists have interesting work of their own to do in ascertaining the distribution of diseases in populations and the natural history of diseases. They are not likely to take the initiative in developing data useful for planning or the formation of public policy. It is necessary to inform them of the data needs of economists and to solicit their cooperation in a joint endeavor.

Classic Design and Other Devices

There is increasing evidence of a rise in interest in evaluation studies conducted without the classic design of study and control groups selected at random. Insistence on classic design is believed to be a hopeless cause: in the health field it is unethical to deprive people in need of services that are likely to prove beneficial; the experimental or study group may contaminate the control group; and valuable numbers of observations are discarded in the establishment of the control group.

It has been shown that ingenuity and persistence can succeed in performing valid evaluations without recourse to classic design. In evaluating the work of a summer encampment for citizenship, substitute controls were established or found by Hyman, Wright, and Hopkins (1962) through recourse to past evaluations of similar programs; by obtaining data for the period preceding the study; by building in small control groups for limited experimental purposes; and by providing for future replication of the study.

Rossi (1966) has emphasized the usefulness of quick and dirty studies in the exploratory phase of a problem. Shapiro (1967) rates highly the indirect approach to studies of end results, provided that "reasonable" criteria are accepted in controlling for extraneous differentials between comparison groups.

In the mental health field, it seems to me, the problem of evaluation is appreciably complicated by the lack of agreement on patients' diagnoses, as well as on health status after treatment. The Hollingshead-Redlich (1958) findings on class differences in diagnosis and treatment hardly point to a ready resolution of the problem. Rather, it may be sensible to act as if the difficulty will persist for some time and the results produced by mental health services will continue to escape precise identification and measurement.

In this situation it is necessary to reconsider whether the classic device of random assignment of patients to study and control groups is so impracticable after all (Paul, 1967). With classic design it is not necessary for the product to be defined. The only important requirement is that all patients originating in a designated area be screened at a central point of entry into the psychiatric-care system and steered to its several alternative facilities. With the advent of the multifaceted community mental health center, the observance of such a requirement does not seem to be nearly so far-fetched as it might have been formerly (NIMH, 1964).

In any case, as Ginzberg (1966a) has pointed out, it is imperative to conduct systematic follow-up of the patient discharged from treatment if we are ever to learn what actually transpired during treatment.

CHANGES IN REQUIREMENTS AND SUPPLY

When programs have been evaluated and priorities determined, the manpower implications follow. These can be determined in stages.

The first stage is to spell out the manpower component of the cost side of the programs that have been selected for implementation. This component has been built in from the beginning of the analysis or can be obtained from staffing guides, assuming that these are consistent with the estimates of cost. In effect, a table of organization is specified for each program and these are aggregated for all programs.

The next stage is to consider the possibility of changing the accepted or existing tables of organization. Two vehicles can be identified: (1) substitution among categories of personnel; and (2) future increases in productivity.

Substitution

I claim no special competence in mental health programs and their staffing. However, it may be useful to offer some generalization drawn from other areas, upon the understanding that the comparability of labor markets must be ascertained empirically.

Much more so than clinicians, economists are partial to the possibilities of substitution among factors of production (Hiestand, 1966; Musgrave, 1965, p. 14; Somers and Somers, 1967, pp. 14–17). While clinicians and administrators view necessary departures from prescribed staffing patterns as makeshifts, which are to be terminated at the earliest opportunity, economists regard such adjustments as empirical verification of their beliefs.

Substituting cheaper personnel with less training for more expensive personnel is always a desirable objective from an economic standpoint. Opportunities for substitution are greater when the scale of output is large than when small (Fein, 1967, p. 111). A finer division of labor is then possible, as is more intensive specialization.

I regard as wholesome the economists' emphasis on the possibilities of substitution in the health services. Nevertheless, close observation of the health field leads me to point out some limitations to this process.

Adam Smith's example of the pin factory as the archetype of specialization and division of labor was a routine operation in which all phases of production could be scheduled. When patient admissions are random, as in an emergency, operations research has shown that it is more efficient to provide service through broadly trained personnel capable of performing more than a single function (Thompson, Avant, and Spiker, 1960).

Another limitation on the possibilities of substitution is the geographic distribution of health personnel. The danger exists that some of the less qualified personnel will locate in areas where suitable supervision is lacking. Physicians and others with advanced training are inclined to locate at medical centers and in large cities.

It is realized, moreover, that changes in personnel may by themselves change the contents of programs and, therefore, the outcome (Musgrave, 1965, p. 15). To acknowledge this is not to say that the change is necessarily an adverse one.

Productivity

If productivity increases, a given input (labor and materials) can produce a larger output, or a smaller input can produce the same output. Changes in productivity depend on changes in knowledge and technology; on changes in the quality of inputs, including educational level; and on the efficiency of the production process, including rate of utilization of capacity and the skill with which management combines the several inputs. The productivity of a given category of personnel depends also on the quantity of other resources by which it is supported.

New drugs have served to render many patients amenable to psychiatric treatment. The open-door policy in mental hospitals, which was adopted at about the same time, is a contributing factor in the apparently increased effectiveness of treatment. Just how much improvement has occurred is not clear (Ginzberg, 1966a).

Another example of an increase in the productivity of psychiatrists is taken from the field of care for the aged. Here the major use of psychiatrists' time is in teaching and counseling the staffs of agencies, rather than in treating patients directly. Whether the two uses of the psychiatrists' time produce the same effect on patients is not known.

A word of caution, perhaps an obvious one, seems to be in order. The very fact that treatment has become more effective makes it accessible to more persons and tends to make it desired by still more persons. In looking ahead, it is not safe to neglect either the demand or the supply side of the equation; the cost-benefit approach makes this clear. The point is introduced here and applies only to the extent that future changes in productivity have not been incorporated in the cost-benefit analysis.

Elasticity of Supply

A few additional comments on the supply of personnel pertaining to the number of workers recruited may be in order. For a given occupation the supply of personnel depends on the monetary remuneration offered, the nonpecuniary advantages and disadvantages, the nearest (best) alternatives for employment, and obstacles to movement into and out of the occupation (Klarman, 1965a, pp. 74–78). Obstacles may exist within a field, as exemplified, perhaps, by psychiatrists in the state mental hospitals and psychoanalysts in the private sector. Once a job is taken, the occupant may see himself in one of two separate markets.

For a given occupation the elasticity of supply is always greater in the long run than in the short run (Yett, 1965). However, such supply is closely linked to the pool of manpower on which it draws. Thus, psychiatry draws on physicians, mostly the recent graduates, psychology on college graduates, psychiatric nursing on the total inventory of registered nurses and practical nurses, psychiatric social workers on the total number of social workers, etc.

For each personnel category it is necessary to ascertain its composition, including such characteristics as age, sex, education, marital status, and its relative responsiveness to monetary and other types of specific inducement (Hiestand, 1966, p. 162). It is likely that responsiveness to additional monetary incentives will vary not only with the amount of the incentive but also with the level of earnings already attained.

SUMMARY AND IMPLICATIONS

In this paper some current approaches to health manpower planning are reviewed and appraised, and a conceptual framework is set forth for looking at the mental health manpower problem within the context of cost-benefit analysis, broadly defined. Throughout, the emphasis is on knowing or ascertaining the outcome of health service programs, for the process of economic valuation is superimposed on the underlying technological data provided by clinicians or epidemiologists.

The plea is for realism in claims made in behalf of mental health programs. Several gains ensue from such realism. Resources are used where they are effective, and removed from where they are not productive. Future requests for additional resources gain in credibility. Above all, lack of knowledge occasions a search for the required knowledge.

In turn, the acquisition of pertinent knowledge depends on the specification of goals. Nothing useful is to be gained from programs or demonstrations aimed to do good. If the criteria of accomplishment are spelled out, it becomes possible to determine whether they have been attained.

The worthwhileness of calculating economic values, especially on the benefit side, depends on the validity of the data on outcome, which link the inputs and outputs of service programs. If the findings on outcome are erroneous or weak, the economic analysis based on them is an idle exercise. Conversely, when the underlying factual foundation is firm, economic analysis can make an important contribution to the optimum (best possible) allocation of resources.

The type of contribution that economics makes will depend on the ability to put a value on the intangible benefits of health. When that is feasible, a full-fledged cost-benefit analysis is in order and the decision-maker can be confronted with a recommended set of priorities. When important components go unmeasured, the analysis takes the form of cost effectiveness, which yields less information than does cost benefit. The decision-maker is given the costs of alternative ways of accomplishing a specified objective, which is determined through other means.

Here the possibilities of substitution among personnel loom important. Economists are impressed by the ability of administrators to adapt to personnel "shortages" by upgrading some employees and by tapping new sources of supply. The diversity of adaptations actually made affords an opportunity to compare differential effects on outcome, if any.

In the care of mental illness, the special problem exists of indeterminacy of both diagnosis and prognosis. Here the classic design of experiments is not only the ideal instrument, it is perhaps the only one that will yield conclusive knowledge of outcome. Such a design has been rendered increasingly practicable by the advent of the multifaceted community mental health center, which can serve as the central point for screening and referring patients.

Knowledge of outcome, combined with appropriate economic valuation, is at the heart of rational planning for mental health manpower. The task of personnel is to provide services in accordance with the values put on them by society. Persons are not employed to discharge professional or agency goals. Nor are they merely holding jobs in order to raise the level of employment and national income.

REFERENCES

ARROW, K. J. 1963. Uncertainty and the welfare economics of medical care. *American Economic Review*, 53:941–973.

BAMBERGER, L. 1965. Financing mental health services and facilities: problems, prospects, and some policy proposals. In *Till we have built Jerusalem*. Washington, D.C.: National Institutes on Rehabilitation and Health Services.

BANE, F. 1959. (Chairman, Surgeon General's Consultant Group on Medical Education.) *Physicians for a growing America*. Washington, D.C.: U.S. Government Printing Office.

BLANK, D. S., and G. J. STIGLER. 1957. *The demand and supply of scientific personnel*. New York: National Bureau of Economic Research.

BORLAND, M., and D. E. YETT. 1966. *Trends in the return on investments in higher education, 1949–1959*. Los Angeles: Authors.

BOULDING, K. E. 1954. An economist's view of the manpower concept. In *National Manpower Council, Proceedings of a conference on the utilization of scientific and professional manpower*. New York: Columbia University Press.

BURKHEAD, J. 1956. *Government budgeting*. New York: Wiley.

CLARK, J. M. 1949. *Guideposts in time of change*. New York: Harper.

DICKINSON, F. G. 1950. *The alleged shortage of physicians*. Chicago: AMA.

FEIN, R. 1958. *Economics of mental illness*. New York: Basic Books.

———. 1967. *The doctor shortage*. Washington, D.C.: Brookings Institution.

FELDSTEIN, M. S. 1966. *Measuring the costs and benefits of health services*. Copenhagen: World Health Organization.

FRIEDMAN, M., and S. KUZNETS. 1945. *Income from independent professional practice*. New York: National Bureau of Economic Research.

FUCHS, V. R. 1966. The contribution of health services to the American economy. *Milbank Memorial Fund Quarterly*, 44 (4, Part 2):65–101.

GANS, H. J. 1967. Planning—and city planning—for mental health. In H. W. Eldredge (Ed.), *Taming megalopolis*. Vol. 2. Garden City, N.Y.: Anchor Books.

GINZBERG, E. 1966a. Manpower and mental health. In Northeast State Governments Conference on Mental Health, *Toward continuity of care: staffing and financing*. Chicago: Council of State Governments.

———. 1966b. Physician shortage reconsidered. *New England Journal of Medicine*, 275 (2):85–87.

GLASSER, M. A. 1965. Prepayment for psychiatric illness. In *Till we have built Jerusalem*. Washington, D.C.: National Institutes on Rehabilitation and Health Services.

GROSS, M. L. 1967. *The doctors*. New York: Dell.

HANSEN, W. L. 1964. Shortages and investment in health manpower. In *The economics of health and medical care*. Ann Arbor: Bureau of Public Health Economics, University of Michigan.

———. 1967. The economics of scientific and engineering manpower. *Journal of Human Resources*, 2:191–215.

HARRIS, S. E. 1964. *The economics of American medicine.* New York: Macmillan.

HIESTAND, D. L. 1966. Research into manpower for health service. *Milbank Memorial Fund Quarterly,* 44 (4, Part 2) :146–179.

HOLLINGSHEAD, A. B. 1960. Social class and mental illness, findings and implications. In N. P. Dellis and H. K. Stone (Eds.), *The training of psychotherapists.* Baton Rouge: Louisiana State University Press.

———, and F. C. REDLICH. 1958. *Social class and mental illness: a community study.* New York: Wiley.

HOLTMANN, A. G. 1965. Another look at the shortage of physicians. *Industrial and Labor Relations Review,* 18:423–424.

HYMAN, H. H., C. R. WRIGHT, and T. K. HOPKINS. 1962. *Applications of methods of evaluation.* Berkeley: University of California Press.

JUDEK, S. 1964. *Medical manpower in Canada.* Ottawa: Queen's Printer.

KLARMAN, H. E. 1951. Requirements for physicians. *American Economic Review, Papers and Proceedings,* 41:633–645.

———. 1965a. *The economics of health.* New York: Columbia University Press.

———. 1965b. Socioeconomic impact of heart disease. In Second National Conference on Cardiovascular Disease, *The heart and circulation.* Vol. 2. Washington, D.C.: Federation of American Societies for Experimental Biology.

———. 1965c. Syphilis control programs. In R. Dorfman (Ed.), *Measuring benefits of government investments.* Washington, D.C.: Brookings Institution.

———, J. O. FRANCIS, and G. D. ROSENTHAL. 1968. Cost effectiveness analysis applied to the treatment of chronic renal disease. *Medical care.* In press.

LEE, R. I., and L. W. JONES. 1933. *The fundamentals of good medical care.* Chicago: University of Chicago Press.

LEES, D. S. 1960. The economics of health services. *Lloyds Bank Review,* 56 (N.S.) : 26–40.

McCAFFREE, K. M. 1966. The cost of mental health care under changing treatment methods. *American Journal of Public Health,* 56:1013–1025.

———. 1967. *The economic basis for the development of community mental health programs.* Seattle: Author.

McKEAN, R. 1958. *Efficiency in government through systems analysis.* New York: Wiley.

MISHLER, E. G., and N. A. SCOTCH. 1965. Sociocultural factors in the epidemiology of schizophrenia. *International Journal of Psychiatry,* 1:258–295.

MOUNTIN, J. W., E. H. PENNELL, and A. G. BERGER. 1949. *Health service areas: estimates of future physician requirements.* Washington, D.C.: U.S. Government Printing Office.

MUSGRAVE, R. A. (Conference chairman). 1965. *Economics of health.* Bethesda, Md.: National Institutes of Health.

MUSHKIN, S. J. 1962. Health as an investment. *Journal of Political Economy,* 70 (5, Part 2) :129–157.

———. 1964. Why health economics? In *The economics of health and medical care.* Ann Arbor: Bureau of Public Health Economics, University of Michigan.

———, and F. D'A. COLLINGS. 1959. Economic costs of disease and injury. *Public Health Reports,* 74:795–809.

National Commission on Community Health Services. 1967. Task Force on Health Manpower, *Health manpower: action to meet community needs.* Washington, D.C.: Public Affairs Press.

National Institute of Mental Health. 1964. *The comprehensive community mental health center.* Washington, D.C.: U.S. Government Printing Office.

PAUL, G. P. 1967. Strategy of outcome research in psychotherapy. *Journal of Consulting Psychology,* 31:109–118.

PREST, A. R., and R. TURVEY. 1965. Cost-benefit analysis: a survey. *Economic Journal,* 300:683–735.

RAYACK, E. 1964. The supply of physicians' services. *Industrial and Labor Relations Review,* 17:221–237.

———. 1965. The shortage of physicians' services. *Industrial and Labor Relations Review,* 18:584–587.

REDER, M. W. 1967. *Problems in the measurement of productivity in the medical care industry.* New York: National Bureau of Economic Research.

RICE, D. P. 1966. *Estimating the cost of illness.* Washington, D.C.: U.S. Government Printing Office.

ROEMER, M. I. 1961. Bed supply and hospital utilization: a natural experiment. *Hospitals,* 35 (21) :36–42.

ROSENTHAL, G. D. 1964. *The demand for general hospital facilities.* Chicago: American Hospital Association.

ROSSI, P. H. 1966. Boobytraps and pitfalls in the evaluation of social action programs. *Proceedings of the Social Statistics Section, American Statistical Association,* 1966. Washington, D.C.: The Association.

ROTHENBERG, J. 1965. Urban renewal programs. In R. Dorfman (Ed.), *Measuring benefits of government investments.* Washington, D.C.: Brookings Institution.

———. 1967. *Economic evaluation of urban renewal.* Washington, D.C.: Brookings Institution.

SCHILLING, T. C. 1966. *The life you save may be your own.* Washington, D.C.: Brookings Institution.

SHAPIRO, S. 1967. End result measurement of quality of medical care. *Milbank Memorial Fund Quarterly,* 45 (2, Part 1) :7–30.

SIMMONS, O. G. 1958. *Social status and public health.* New York: Social Science Research Council.

SOMERS, H. M., and A. R. SOMERS. 1967. *A program for research in health economics.* Washington, D.C.: U.S. Government Printing Office.

STICKLE, G. 1965. What priority, human life? *American Journal of Public Health,* 55:1692–98.

STIGLER, G. J. 1952. *The theory of price.* (Rev. ed.) New York: Macmillan.

THOMPSON, J. B., O. W. AVANT, and E. D. SPIKER. 1960. How queuing theory works for the hospital. *Modern Hospital,* 94 (3) :75–78.

WEISBROD, B. A. 1961. *Economics of public health.* Philadelphia: University of Pennsylvania Press.

WEISS, J. H. 1966. *The changing job structure of health manpower.* Cambridge, Mass.: Department of Economics, Harvard University.

YETT, D. E. 1965. The supply of nurses: an economist's view. *Hospital Progress,* 46:88–102.

———. 1968. *An economic analysis of the hospital nursing shortage.* Washington, D.C.: U.S. Government Printing Office.

YOUNG, W. O. 1961. Dental health. In B. S. Hollingshead (Ed.), *The survey of dentistry.* Washington, D.C.: American Council on Education.

ZUBIN, J. 1964. Discussion. In P. H. Hoch and J. Zubin (Eds.), *The evaluation of psychiatric treatment.* New York: Grune and Stratton.

CHAPTER 5

The Relation of Conceptual
Models of Disturbed Behavior
to Institutional and
Manpower Requirements

GEORGE W. ALBEE

IN THE SCOPE OF A SHORT chapter it is not feasible to review the rise and fall of the prescientific models that Western man developed to explain disturbed and disturbing behavior in his fellow-man. Nor is there space for an examination of the contemporary explanatory models held by cultures outside our own Western industrialized societies. Such a neglect of history, and such cultural chauvinism, must necessarily restrict and narrow these speculations and observations. On the other hand, the conference for which these remarks are prepared is concerned primarily with exploring mental health manpower solutions to urgent contemporary problems in our society, problems that exist today and will exist tomorrow.

We tend to be impatient with the slowness of our progress in solving these massive and perplexing human problems. Let me remind you that although the earth itself has existed for a long time, some form of man has lived here for only the past million years. And human beings as we know them have been here for only the past 100,000 years or so. If we make the age of the earth equivalent to a 24-hour day, then man has been around for just the past three seconds, and the scientific era has lasted for about the last eye blink in time.

But science is our best hope. Our progress in the past 250 years in discovering lawful and predictable relationships has exceeded that of all the ages that have gone before. While there is a kind of romantic satisfaction in looking at prescientific explanations of disturbed behavior, some of which have a kind of poetic or symbolic validity, scientific explanations, once achieved, are not likely to be abandoned.

Most conceptual models in our field are less than neat; they are not well organized and they are not mutually exclusive. Any attempt to separate our models into consistent and circumscribed compartments is fraught with all sorts of dangers.

With these conventional genuflexions about the desirability of logic and consistency out of the way, I will go ahead with some fairly loose characterizations of current models in psychopathology. Models are important because they have direct effects on the forms of our institutional care-delivery systems, which in turn dictate manpower demands.

I make no pretense to being unbiased in this effort. I am by temperament and education an environmentalist, living in a scientific world ruled by a model that I find incompatible. In attempting to argue for alternative models, however, I have no intent to imply that knowledge has reached the point where any road should be closed.

Professionals in the so-called mental health professions are concerned almost exclusively with human behavior. The behavior they must try to explain, with rare exceptions, is disturbing, worrisome, unsympathetic, peculiar, hard to understand, and atypical. But it is behavior. Ordinarily, it involves motor movements of the skeletal musculature and other muscle systems usually under voluntary control. The disturbing behavior may include gross movements (grimacing, wringing the hands, curling into a fetal position, stereotyped acts endlessly repeated), as well as speech that ranges from garbled word-salads to grammatically correct reports of delusional thinking, to reports of peculiar thought processes, to reports of generalized anxiety. It includes verbal or motor responses to standardized test situations. But it is behavior. It is behavior that our models must explain and relate to other behavior, and it is behavior that leads to inferences about inner processes. While there are exceptions to this general rule, they are relatively unimportant in frequency and significance. (Diagnostic efforts may occasionally seek stigmata, or measure palmar sweating, or record any changes in the blood pressure, as part of an assessment.)

In contrast, nonpsychiatric medical diagnoses more usually require a variety of observations, which may not involve behavior. Urinalysis, X rays, throat cultures, and inflammations, rashes, high temperature—none of these important elements of a diagnosis, in the usual medical sense, is behavioral.

As a consequence of the central importance of behavior as the starting point for a science of psychopathology, it may be worthwhile to examine some of the logical possibilities that exist for the utilization of such data.

Kenneth Spence (1956) argued that a science of behavior of organisms focuses attention on the relations between behavior and two other classes of events—earlier or concomitant *environmental stimulation* and *organic conditions.*

Attention is focused on: (1) *response variables* (R), which involve behavioral descriptions or measurements of characteristics throughout the range of behavior of subjects; (2) *stimulus variables* (S), qualitative or quantitative descriptions or manipulations of the physical or social environment in which the subject behaves; and (3) *organic variables* (O), which are either qualitative or objective measurements of the anatomical and physiological characteristics of the subject.

Attempts are made to find lawful relationships among these different classes of variables. Spence organized the possible relationships and the types of discoverable laws as follows:

CLASS I LAWS

Class I laws involve $R=f(R)$ relationships. Certain kinds of behavior are concomitant with or predictive of other kinds of behavior. For example, in the field of psychopathology, certain key behaviors (symptoms) are found to be associated with other behavior that society has decided is unacceptable and justifies intervention. On the other hand, certain other classes of behavior (concern for others, postponing immediate pleasure for future gains, etc.) are found to be associated with positive adjustment. Class I approaches would include tests, interviews, factor-analytic approaches, and time samples for the prediction of other behavior. The development of mathematical models and computer simulation in recent years would be in this area.

CLASS II LAWS

Class II laws involve $R=f(S)$ relationships. As Spence pointed out, there are two subclasses here. The first subclass involves current environmental events, and the second involves events that have occurred in the more distant past. In the first case the interest of the psychopathologist might be in relating the changed responses of a subject in psychotherapy to the behavior of the therapist, or the changes in behavior of a back-ward schizophrenic in response to token rewards. In the case of behavior resulting from environmental events in the more distant past, the psychopathologist might be interested in determining the relations between present behavioral symptoms and reports of early childhood experiences, often accounts of family relationships that occurred many years before. Most laws that involve learning, and inferences about social motivation, belong to this subclass. It is certainly the broadest, loosest, and most varied.

Arguments about intervention strategy are developing between the observers who attribute primary importance to events that have occurred in the individual's distant past, and those who deemphasize the distant past to focus on the present. Because of the growing importance of this theoretical difference within this diverse group, I will illustrate it with quotes from spokesmen for the two approaches.

Bettelheim (1967) says:

Despite the incredible variety of symptoms among the several hundred schizophrenic children we have worked with over the years, they all shared one thing in common: an unremitting fear for their lives. This takes us, for the moment, beyond the narrower group of autistic children. The reason for this is my stated conviction that all psychotic children suffer from the experience of having been subject to extreme conditions of living, and that the severity of their disturbance is directly related to how early in life these conditions arose, for how long they obtained, and how severe was their impact on the child (p. 63).

Understanding the historical causation of later disturbed behavior leads to interventions planned to correct, insofar as possible, the underlying problems that interfere with social behavior. A different point of view is expressed by Eysenck (1957):

Symptoms are learned S-R connections; once they are extinguished or deconditioned, treatment is complete. Such treatment is based exclusively on present factors; like Lewin's theory, this one is a-historical. Non-verbal methods are favored over verbal ones, although a minor place is reserved for verbal methods of extinction and reconditioning. Concern is with *function*, not *content*. The main difference between the two theories arises over the question of "symptomatic" treatment. According to orthodox theory, this is useless unless the underlying complexes are attacked. According to the present theory, there is no evidence for these putative complexes, and symptomatic treatment is all that is required (pp. 267–268).

Both of these approaches emphasize learning, and both stress relearning as therapy. The disagreement involves the question about the importance of unraveling the individual's history to arrive at an understanding of underlying causes of present behavior.

CLASS III LAWS

Class III laws involve $O = f(S)$ relationships. This is the only class in which behavior may be left out of the formula. In the case of psychopathology, studies of the effects of isolation on blood pressure, or observations of the effects of controlled environmental pressure in the production of psychosomatic symptoms, might be illustrative.

CLASS IV LAWS

Class IV laws involve $R = f(O)$ relationships. It is the identification of this sort of relationship that is the goal of the reductionist, who seeks in the molecular substructure at a biochemical level, or in the functioning of the central nervous system, the endocrine system, the metabolic system, etc., factors associated with or causing behavior. In the field of psychopathology, a significant number of investigators have insisted on the primary importance of this class of relationships. It is here that the most outstanding scientific successes in medicine generally have occurred. Medical research has uncovered important, often critical, relationships between underlying organic factors and symptoms. It is natural, and predictable, that those psychiatrists most identified with medical tradition would argue that this area of search for new relationships should occupy the center of the stage in psychopathology and should be supported maximally.

Below is an example of this point of view, as expressed by Heath (1960) :

We consider schizophrenia to be a genetically determined metabolic disease, or, more specifically, a disease characterized by alterations in the metabolic pathway for the breakdown of certain (as yet unidentified) endogenously occurring compounds. Our current hypothesis, based on our most recent data, is that the genetic defect is manifest by the presence of a qualitatively different protein (taraxein) in the blood stream. A toxic compound formed as a result of the interfering presence of taraxein alters physiological activity in specific parts of the brain, with associated behavioral changes. From our data, we postulate that these changes develop because the protein substance impairs enzymatic activity in a pathway related (in an undetermined way, as yet) to the metabolism of amines. Our current studies suggest that histamine may be implicated, either directly or indirectly, in the faulty metabolic process (p. 146).

The two most currently important approaches in psychopathology involve the search for $R = f(S)$ relationships and that for $R = f(O)$ relationships.

In terms of scientific manpower, the largely environmentalist group seeking $R = f(S)$ relationships is the more heterogeneous and eclectic, with a fair amount of communication, mutual acceptance, toleration, and even shared interests and values among them. They count among their ranks the cultural anthropologists, the broadly psychoanalytic theorists and therapists, the social epidemiologists, the social workers, the clinical and social psychologists, and the social and community psychiatrists. Because of diverse professional identifications, and the powerful pulls of professional loyalties, there also is much ambivalence among members of this broad group toward each other, but essentially they speak the same family of languages and have the same general orientation: disturbed behavior largely is learned, is continuous with normal behavior, and reflects disturbing environmental experiences.

In recent years another group has appeared on the $R=f(S)$ scene—the operant technologists, or behavior therapists, who fiercely assert that the only path to scientific salvation is to be found in the manipulation of immediate environmental events that shape behavior; they look with some interest toward education as a potential ally.

A number of other variations on the $R=f(S)$ approach, relying on hypothetical constructs, may be best labeled motivational models. They are exemplified by Maslow's (1954) conception of a hierarchy of motives, which infers from behavior the presence of internal driving forces that make man more than a responding automaton. Frustration of motives is thought to cause behavioral disturbances. Maslow (1954), Fromm-Reichmann (1950), Herzberg (1966), and Jahoda (1958), to name a few, each suggest in somewhat different language, but in an essentially similar way, that while man is continuous with lower animals, shares with other species a striving for homeostasis, and actively searches for conditions that insure personal and racial safety, he ascends to levels of complexity beyond any other species in matters of self-awareness, anticipation of the future, and needs for self-expression and creativity. Herzberg (1966) has shown that deprivation of "hygiene" needs causes human misery and unhappiness but that satisfaction of these needs, while removing unhappiness, does not result in a sense of satisfaction or growth. He makes the further intriguing suggestion that neurotic behavior is a kind of frantic search for hygienic and creature comforts as a source of happiness. Only when man has opportunities to do those things he is best capable of doing, only when he has the uniquely human experience of a struggle toward creative expression and ultimate personal attainment, does he sense positive meaning in his life.

In the second major group, those seeking $R=f(O)$ relationships, the scientific manpower required follows (with exceptions) from the logical premises of a more restricted organic-illness model. Because disturbed behavior is believed by this group to be caused by disturbed or diseased processes at the molecular or other organic level, research and intervention usually must be structural and, therefore, largely biomedical, broadly defined. Manpower demands are for highly skilled technicians and physical scientists—physicians, biochemists, psychopharmacologists, etc., and there is relatively less inclination to welcome the behavioral scientists and social scientists except as useful ancillary helpers in diagnosis or in research efforts aimed at identifying the discontinuous categories of people who must be studied or treated.

In my reading of the arguments of proponents of these two general approaches, I find there is a subtle but pervasive intolerance toward the other group on the part of many of the organicists.

Almost without exception the environmentalist says in effect, "I am not sure I am right. I think the organic approach is going to be unproductive, but I certainly would not try to prevent them from continuing to look for an underlying organic cause." On the other hand, the organicists seem more certain they are right. Many of their statements suggest a premature conviction that all abnormal behavior must be rooted in abnormal biology, that there is, in Gerard's (1960) words, "no twisted thought without a twisted molecule."

This situation is understandable. The organic, $R=f(O)$, position is closely related to the illness model. The definition of disturbed behavior as illness enjoys a current primacy and gives greatest responsibility, prestige, and control to the institutions and manpower demanded by this model. Understandably, any suggestion of lack of validity to the model is threatening to the establishment and must be resisted. The position of the organically oriented group is illustrated in the paper of Walter Barton (1965), medical director of the American Psychiatric Association, reporting on the Second National Congress on Mental Illness and Health sponsored by the American Medical Association. He says, "It is significant and important that the Congress underscored that community mental health programs are basically medical programs and must therefore have the leadership and guidance of individual physicians and medical organizations" (p. 7).

Dr. Barton further cautions against the danger that an overenthusiasm for community psychiatry may dilute medical responsibility and control: "Again and again participants pointed out the danger that, in our current enthusiasm for community psychiatry, policies and procedures may be developed without medical guidance. The result would be to introduce medically unsound policies, which would delay improvement of psychiatric care and bring the whole program into disrepute as inept practices become apparent to the public" (p. 7).

Perhaps the crucial question underlying these different approaches is whether all human behavior, normal and abnormal, is *continuous*, or whether a number of *discontinuous* mental diseases exists. The illness model often must defend the discontinuity position, which argues for separate and discrete mental diseases, each with its own cause, prognosis, and treatment.

But an environmental $R=f(S)$ approach, implicit in most molar psychological human interaction models, does not see in abnormal behavior anything more than an exaggeration or distortion of the normal, understandable as a natural, learned process, usually originating in unfortunate social experiences.

Of course, sophisticated proponents of an organic model need not defend the extreme position that all disturbed behavior is truly discontinuous. Extremes of endocrinological variability, or neural responsiveness, can be labeled disease even in the absence of a definable interruption of continuously varying function.

But there is still an important distinction, I would argue, between a model that conceives of abnormal behavior as learned disturbed behavior in interpersonal relationships and one that suggests a defective or damaged capacity for effective interpersonal relationships. In the first case, preventive or remedial approaches might focus on strengthening the family through social action or on reinforcement schedules shaping and maintaining effective and reciprocal behavioral sequences between interacting human beings; in the second case, a search would be made for some innate or acquired discrete defect within the individual, either genetically or historically produced, which requires correction before normal interpersonal relationships can be resumed or achieved.

Obviously, these alternative approaches run together at the edges. But the distinction may be worth preserving because of the powerful influence of the model on the nature of our institutions and on subsequent manpower demands.

Where the illness model seeks to identify, prevent, remove, counteract, neutralize, or correct the underlying defect causing the disturbed behavior, an environmental-social-learning model seeks to provide a more supportive and hygienic environment, and strives to encourage, nurture, reinforce, and strengthen those behaviors in the individual that are positive goal-seeking and self-actualizing. The physician traditionally corrects or remedies a condition with the expectation that once normal functioning is reestablished, health will be restored. In a pathology model, those who are not sick are healthy or normal.

The position of the continuity-environmentalist group is expressed by Ullmann and Krasner (1965):

Maladaptive behaviors are learned behaviors, and the development and maintenance of a maladaptive behavior is no different from the development and maintenance of any other behavior. There is no discontinuity between desirable and undesirable modes of adjustment or between "healthy" or "sick" behavior. The first major implication of this view is the question of how a behavior is to be identified as desirable or undesirable, adaptive or maladaptive. The general answer we propose is that because there are no disease entities involved in the majority of subjects displaying maladaptive behavior, the designation of a behavior as pathological or not is dependent upon the individual's society (p. 20).

A very similar position was expressed by another member of this heterogeneous environmentalist group, although her theoretical orientation was quite different. After working for years with schizophrenics, Frieda Fromm-Reichmann (1950) concluded: "It is my belief that the problems and emotional difficulties of mental patients, neurotics and psychotics are in principle rather similar to one another and also to the emotional difficulties in living from which we all suffer at times" (p. xi).

The organicist's answer to such arguments, on the other hand, is illustrated beautifully by the statement entitled "Problems of Health Manpower in Relation to Mental Health," presented by Dale Cameron on behalf of the American Psychiatric Association to the Consumer Panel, National Advisory Commission on Health Manpower (January 5, 1967). He stresses the importance of discrete, discontinuous organic illnesses in justification for preserving the status quo. Dr. Cameron says, in effect, that American psychiatry favors any kind of innovation and experimentation to solve the mental health manpower shortage so long as the psychiatrist remains the ultimate authority.

In his words:

The American Psychiatric Association's approach to the challenge of solving the staffing problem of the community services in the offing is characterized by flexibility, a willingness to experiment, and an acceptance of the inevitability of many changes to come in mental health personnel utilization and practices. . . .

Basically, and in these contexts, it is the position of the American Psychiatric Association that whatever changes may be in store in relation to restructuring the functions and utilization of the several kinds of personnel that must be involved, that one fundamental and time-tested policy would be recognized and respected by all concerned, namely: that physicians have ultimate responsibility for patient care and that they alone are trained to assume this responsibility.

No one can dispute the primary responsibility of the physician in the field of human illness. And as long as disturbed and disturbing behavior is defined as illness, this is the only logical position.

Dr. Cameron says, "Psychiatry is the medical specialty concerned with illnesses marked chiefly by mental symptoms including those associated with physical illnesses."

He goes on:

There is considerable discussion at the present time about the inappropriateness of the medical model in the prevention and treatment of the mental illnesses. There are those who would substitute a "human effectiveness" model, which focuses on social and environmental factors as underlying the onset of neuroses, personality and character problems and other mental disorders. There is much to be said for the conceptual usefulness of the "human effectiveness" model *so long as it is not projected as a displacement of the medical model* but rather as a supplement to it with circumscribed applicability. (Italics added.)

Dr. Cameron now begins the ritual that has been effective so long in reinforcing the belief of legislators and the intelligent lay public of the validity of the "illness model":

A wide range of disorders are subsumed under the general term, mental illness. Genetic factors may play a part. Inborn errors of metabolism are sometimes present and subject to alleviation with appropriate treatment. Problems in prematurity and early infant care have a bearing on later mental symptomatology. Innoculation of the child with measles vaccine may prevent the disabling mental disorder encephalitis. The conquest of pellagra has largely removed the ravages of a dementia due to a vitamin deficiency. Only a relatively few years ago some 12% of all admissions to mental hospitals were due to syphillitic meningoencephalitis. The advent of penicillin proved not only an effective medical treatment for it but also prevented the onset of the disease process in the central nervous system that produced a mental illness. Chronic brain syndromes due to vascular disorders are common in the elderly who have arteriosclerosis and are subject to strokes. The elderly are also subject to depressions that are very often relieved with new drugs and the use of electro-shock therapy. Alcoholic delirium and Korsakoff's psychosis are other examples of medical problems that entail mental illness.

The point of all of this should not be lost. Psychiatry, in insisting on its prerogative of primary responsibility, and control of treatment institutions and intervention, bases its argument both on rare and uncertain genetic and metabolic conditions and on common chronic organic mental conditions, which it characteristically neglects. Much of psychiatric practice is private, much of it is suburban, and most hospital psychiatry is practiced in general hospitals. Few of these "organic" conditions are the focus of current psychiatric treatment. A great majority of the people psychiatrists treat are not suffering from genetic, metabolic, arteriosclerotic, or alcoholic delirium. If psychiatrists were to devote their primary attention to these kinds of cases, there would be little need for debate about models.

Instead, the consequences of the successful promulgation of the organic point of view will be that the Comprehensive Mental Health Centers, the research centers in mental retardation, and all of the other brave new programs for improved care for disturbed children and adults will all founder in much the same way, and for the same reasons that the state hospital system has foundered.

Most of the mental conditions that concern us are chronic and resistant to intervention. This means they must be treated in tax-supported agencies. But, American psychiatry, like American medicine, resists salaried positions in public agencies. The illness model dictates both the nature of the institutions and the kind of personnel required, and these kinds of people do not exist, cannot be recruited, and will never be available.

In his dramatic and stimulating report of his mental health survey of Boston, Ryan (1967) found five kinds of people for whom little or no psychiatric care was available. These included children (and especially those in need of residential treatment), adolescents, the aged, the poor, multiproblem families, and the discharged mental-hospital patients. This list represents almost exactly the groups identified in surveys of Appalachia as those most in need of help. I must ask, parenthetically, if the Boston area, with all its rich psychiatric resources, is neglecting these particular groups, what hope has the illness model to hold out for Appalachia?

Ryan (1967) goes on to say: "The solidly established middle-class white American has an almost infinitely greater chance of obtaining the skilled services of the trained and experienced mental health professional than do poor people. Education, youth, being female—these are additional characteristics that improve one's chances" (p. 51).

To further compound the problem of mismatch between numbers and need, several observers have pointed recently to the fact that the "sickness" label is being applied to more and more human conditions in our society. Milton (1965), for example, and Dunham (1965) have discussed at length the broadening areas of social responsibility being staked out by psychiatry. Formal claims have been filed for primary medical responsibility in the problems of aging, juvenile delinquency, alcoholism, school learning problems, mental retardation, and drug addiction, to name just a few.

As just one example, an organic model has come to dominate the field of mental retardation and mental deficiency. The explanations that now occupy the center of the stage emphasize the need for discovering organic causes and methods of treatment or prevention. The emphasis is on exogenous causation and on research aimed at reducing the frequency of trauma, infection, biochemical imbalance, etc. Important as this model is, we must also face the fact that intelligence in the general population is distributed in a normal curve, and that something like 2 per cent of all children born will be two standard deviations below the mean of the population, even after all the organic causes are discovered and prevented or corrected. This means that if we are seriously interested in helping mentally deficient children, we should be developing educational manpower that will allow the maximum development of whatever potential these children have. Furthermore, we should be spending our energy and money to train at least as many people for intensive educational intervention with the retarded as we now spend to work in educational approaches to students in graduate school education. There are more "normal" children with IQ's below 70 than children with IQ's above 130. Yet, there is a fantastic disproportion between what our society spends on the lifetime education of the bright children as contrasted with what we spend on children below 70. If we believe our myth—that everyone should have the same opportunity to develop his potential to his maximum capacity—then we should take steps to right this imbalance.

The organic or illness model in psychopathology strongly supports the requirement that the institution for intervention with disturbed people be a hospital or clinic, for diagnosis or treatment. As a consequence of the serious and continuing shortage of psychiatrists, there is a growing tendency for mental hygiene clinics, juvenile court clinics, residential treatment centers, and all the range of tax-supported public institutions "treating the emotionally ill" to have only part-time psychiatrists available. In the extreme this can reach the point where a psychiatrist, nominally in charge of all patient diagnosis and treatment, spends as little as one-half day a month at the facility.

There are approximately 2,000 "psychiatric clinics" in the United States. At the present time two thirds of these do not have a single full-time psychiatrist on their staff! There are approximately 300 public state mental hospitals in this country. A recent survey reported by the National Committee Against Mental Illness (1966) found that 21 of them did not have a single psychiatrist on their staff; 91 other state hospitals were found to have only one to four staff psychiatrists. This means that in well over one third of all the public tax-supported mental hospitals run by state governments, psychiatric time is practically unavailable. But, the picture is still further complicated by the fact that something like 50 per cent of the physicians employed in a majority of state hospitals are foreign-born and foreign-trained. Without attempting to judge the adequacy of these "psychiatrists," many with varying degrees of handicap in English, to function effectively in a field where subtle communication is of critical importance, it is safe to say that bringing these foreign physicians to this country represents a "brain drain" on those countries where physicians are in desperately short supply. The largest single supplier of these physicians is the Philippines, followed by India; neither country can afford to spare its physicians.

There are a number of reasons for the persistence of the illness model in the field of functional behavior disorder. I have reviewed these at length elsewhere (Albee, 1967). The illness model developed and was adopted because: (1) it was more compatible with a rising scientific *Zeitgeist* than a sin, or demonic, explanation; (2) the early success in finding the cause of paresis raised hopes that other mental "illnesses" also had a biological cause; (3) early investigations seemed to prove that a genetic factor was important; (4) it was an excuse for putting victims away and out of sight, pending discovery of "a cure"; (5) money could be spent on biological research, thus not upsetting the class hierarchy and preserving the status quo; and, finally, (6) it allowed family and society to avoid a feeling of responsibility and to hold Fate responsible.

Periodically, an announcement is made that a molecular or organic defect has been discovered that is present in a group of mental cases, usually schizophrenics, and not present in matched controls. Few of these claims have stood the test of scientific evaluation. Kety (1965) has reviewed the organic research in schizophrenia and concludes that no one has yet found the mysterious and elusive organic cause.

The most usual defect in the design of this research is the operation of uncontrolled variables that affect the functioning of schizophrenics. For example, the finding that chronic back-ward schizophrenics have hearts smaller than those of matched controls would not lead even the most incautious investigator to conclude that small hearts cause schizophrenia. Schizophrenics get very little exercise and practically everyone knows this. But findings repeatedly are announced that differentiate the blood, the urine, or the brain cells of back-ward schizophrenics from controls, with the implication that cause is involved.

Another persistent argument for an illness model is the fact that some 25 per cent of first admissions to public mental hospitals are diagnosed as suffering from chronic brain syndromes. Is this not proof of the validity of the organic position?

This subject requires thoughtful consideration because it implies that damage to the brain produces disturbed or disturbing behavior.

The research evidence, on the contrary, suggests that there is no significant relationship between the amount of brain tissue destroyed and the degree of resulting personality disorder. Rather, brain damage sometimes results in physical and behavioral incapacities—enfeeblement, impotency, immediate memory loss, etc.—which are themselves stressful and frightening to the individual afflicted. Depending upon his capacity for tolerating stress, and his adaptability, a mental disturbance may follow.

Sophisticated proponents of the organic position ofen deal with evidence supporting the environmental cause or precipitation of disturbed behavior by arguing that an underlying organic susceptibility must be present before environmental stress can lead to breakdown. The trouble with this argument, as it applies to mental disorders, is that there is no way of determining susceptibility in the phenotype until the occurrence of the emotional disorder. It becomes a circular argument, where those who break down were susceptible and those who did not were not.

Still another argument in support of the illness model, and quarantine in asylums, is the allegation that disturbed people are dangerous to society. Again, research reveals the contrary to be true. Former mental patients actually commit significantly fewer crimes than nonpatients. While there is a slightly higher than average suicide rate in this group, it is not especially remarkable.

Drunken drivers represent a far greater danger to society, and probably deserve institutionalization more than schizophrenics, if protection of society, and of themselves, is the criterion.

Even the risk of suicide may be questioned as a sufficient reason for involuntary hospitalization.

John Stuart Mill (1863), in his monumental essay *On Liberty*, is of the opinion that:

. . . the sole end for which mankind are warranted, individually or collectively, in interfering with the liberty of action of any of their number, is self-protection. But the only purpose for which power can be rightfully exercised over any member of a civilized community, against his will, is to prevent harm to others. His own good, either physical or moral, is not a sufficient warrant. He cannot rightfully be compelled to do or forebear because it will be better for him to do so, because it will make him happier, and because, in the opinion of others, to do so would be wise, or even right. These are good reasons for remonstrating with him, or reasoning with him, or persuading him, or entreating him, but not for compelling him, or visiting him with any evil in case he do otherwise. To justify that, the conduct from which it is desired to deter him must be calculated to produce evil to someone else. . . . Over himself, over his own body and mind, the individual is sovereign (p. 23).

There is a still further serious practical defect with the illness model. Scheff (1966) has discussed this problem at length. We take great care in English and American law to insure that an innocent man not be adjudged guilty. We agree, in general, with the dictum that it is better for 1,000 guilty men to go free than for one innocent man to be unjustly hanged. In both law and science, Type I Errors (rejection of the Null hypothesis when it should be accepted) are regarded as more dangerous than Type II Errors (finding no relationship where one exists). The opposite situation obtains in medical practice.

Research has shown that physicians are much more inclined to diagnose disease or pathology where there is none than the reverse. It is understandable that a mis-diagnosis in which a serious condition in a patient is overlooked should be more reprehensible and dangerous than the opposite error, where the physician finds pathology when there is none. Both society and medicine probably like things the way they are in this respect.

But, in psychiatry, the fate of the diagnosed mental patient is often far more personally damaging than is true of other kinds of diagnosed illnesses.

Scheff (1966, pp. 128–168) has shown, for example, that psychiatrists in tax-supported public settings diagnose "mental illness" with a very high frequency on the basis of exceedingly brief interviews, despite the fact that these conditions are acknowledged to be very subtle and difficult to identify. In one study there was evidence that nearly two thirds of the people committed involuntarily to public mental hospitals were neither dangerous nor helpless, the most usual criteria for forcible commitment.

Many of the revolutions in scientific thinking that have occurred have resulted from the sudden perception that some commonly accepted "truth" was not true at all. Abandoning such a truth may result in the toppling of a whole conceptual superstructure. Men's minds often explore restlessly the crowded space inside the walls of fixed ideas. When at last the suggestion is made that a wall be knocked down, man is freed to explore vaster reaches.

The outrage that had followed the publication of Darwin's work reflected the Victorian horror at the suggestion of man's simian ancestry; the distaste for the position that man is continuous with lower forms was probably exceeded only by the revulsion that followed Freud's argument stressing the sexual origins of neurosis and the continuity between the normal and the insane. Freud's position that there existed side by side within man's breast both basic animal instincts and civilized and cultured Victorian control was too much for most Victorians, and continues to be too much for many organicists.

Bruner (1957) describes clearly the situation at the beginning of the twentieth century when he says that:

. . . lawful continuity between man and the animal kingdom, between dreams and unreason on one side and waking rationality on the other, between madness and sanity, between consciousness and unconsciousness, between the mind of the child and the adult mind, between primitive and civilized man—each of these has been a cherished discontinuity preserved in doctrinal canons (p. 278) .

It was hard for most men to relinquish their faith in the discontinuities, to abandon their belief that man was different in kind from the animal, created triumphantly in the image of God, and that those afflicted with insanity were somehow defective or evil.

Eventual acceptance of the continuity environmental-learning position, as a viable alternative model, would lead to rapid changes in the nature of our mental institutions and in the kinds of manpower to staff them.

One consequence that would follow from the development of an alternative social-learning model is the relatively simpler solution to the manpower shortage that a learning model permits. Intervention personnel could include large numbers of bachelor's-level people, trainable in great numbers and at considerably less expense.

There is a current owl-faced platitude, delivered with great pomposity, which says that the social and behavioral sciences seriously lag the physical and biological sciences in knowledge. If only, it is said, we could make faster progress in behavioral science, if only we could learn as much about the human being as we know about the atom, progress could be made in dealing with man's problems with himself and his fellows.

This is far from accurate. We *do* know a great deal in the behavioral sciences, but many of the things we know are threatening to both the establishment and the status quo. For example, we know very well that the nature of the social world of the infant and child in the family is of critical importance in determining subsequent rates of emotional disorder. In our culture, the stable family is the best bulwark against emotional disorder, and efforts at prevention will have to be directed to those social institutions that directly or indirectly affect, positively or negatively, family stability. For hopelessly disrupted families, we must find ways of providing the best possible substitutes for the children affected.

If alternative models are tolerated and supported, there will still be plenty of mental illness for the organically minded psychiatrist to work with. All of the emotional problems associated with progressive central nervous system malfunctioning, the problems of the organically induced disturbances in general, of seizure states, and of toxic and endocrinologically induced psychoses will be left.

Also left are other responsibilities clearly in the medical area. For example, problems of prematurity and perinatal care do indeed have an effect on subsequent mental conditions. The Negro child born in a tax-supported, understaffed city hospital to a "medically indigent" mother who has received little or no prenatal care, and who is pushed out of the hospital as soon as possible with her baby, is subjected to medically unsound treatment. The baby she bears weighs, on the average, significantly less than babies born to middle-class mothers. This innocent child is ten to fifteen times more likely, later in his life, to be called schizophrenic or mentally retarded.

It is ironic that "organic factors" are used to justify medical control of later intervention efforts when the conditions are traceable to such damaging early experiences. Parenthetically, too few of us are aware that when an indigent woman in advanced labor is brought to an urban general hospital for emergency delivery, she will generally receive assistance in the delivery of her baby but be turned out six to eight hours afterward.

Once the hypothesis is allowed that most neurotic and functionally psychotic behavior may represent learned patterns, the institutions that could be developed to deal with these may well be *educational* in nature. It is already widely demonstrated that behavioral modification techniques can prevent or interrupt the desocialization that occurs on the back wards of state hospitals. By using college graduates with some special training in reeducational techniques, it would be possible for society to develop new institutional forms that require manpower rather easily recruited and trained. While it is difficult to describe institutions not yet conceived, it is possible that they will be combinations of present day-care centers and night hospitals recast as small tax-supported state adult schools with a heavy emphasis on occupational therapy, reeducation, and rehabilitation.

Albert Bandura (1967) has a similar vision. He says:

The day may not be far off when psychological disorders will be treated not in hospitals or mental hygiene clinics but in comprehensive "learning centers," when clients will be considered not patients suffering from hidden psychic pathologies but responsible people who participate actively in developing their own potentialities (p. 86).

Unless we develop a viable alternative to the illness model as an explanation of mental disorder, we must face the next several decades with the realistic understanding that the mental health manpower picture is going to worsen because we cannot train enough professionals to meet the manpower needs of the institutions this model demands.

By the year 2000, just 31 years from now, the population of the United States, estimated conservatively, will be 350 million. Many of our states are growing much more rapidly than the underdeveloped countries whose population boom haunts the nightmares of social planners and liberal intellectuals. Not only is our population increasing much more rapidly than our professional and institutional mental health resources; but also there are relatively few signs that any really serious action in professional education is contemplated that could narrow the gap. Indeed, the gap will widen steadily.

Medicine and psychiatry are the central examples to illustrate this point. At the present time some 7,500 new U.S. medical school graduates enter internships each year. But the population of the United States is growing by more than 3 million each year. In order to provide enough physicians to take care of this population increase alone at the same doctor-to-patient ratio as currently prevails, we would need almost exactly 4,000 new physicians a year. Thus, it seems as though we are gaining something like 3,000 new medical doctors a year. This erroneous assumption has been made by a number of distinguished people. It neglects to take into account the frequently unrecognized fact that doctors are not immortal. They die, retire, or otherwise leave the field, in the same way as other professionals. We must add to the number neeeded to take care of the population increase enough to replace those leaving practice.

It is very difficult to get an accurate figure of the percentage of physicians who leave practice each year. The National Education Association (Albee, 1963, p. 91) has worked out with great care an estimate of the rate at which professors are lost and has arrived at 6 per cent as the best estimate. Perhaps it would be safe to use a much more conservative 3 per cent for physicians. (This suggests that the *average* length of practice for doctors is 33 years, which does not seem unreasonable.) At this rate of loss our nation currently would require some 7,000 new physicians a year as replacements. Adding 4,000 and 7,000, we arrive at a need for 11,000 to stay even. Now we see that instead of gaining doctors we are losing them, and at a frighteningly rapid rate.

What is going to be done about this growing shortage of physicians in the face of a rising population curve? Not much. The Association of American Medical Colleges estimates that fourteen years elapse between the decision to start a new medical school and the commencement day for its first class (Albee, 1959, pp. 105–113). It is a very expensive undertaking to establish a new medical school, but, even with the money in hand, time has a way of slipping by while architects are drawing plans, school buildings and laboratories are being constructed, university hospitals are being organized or built and staffed, faculty members are being recruited (and medical school faculties are plagued presently with unfilled positions), and students are being selected and enrolled for a four-year sequence.

What about psychiatry? Psychiatry is a specialty within medicine. Most medical specialties report serious shortages, and few of them are able to fill their available residencies. Psychiatry must compete with other medical specialties where shortages and attractive inducements attempt to lure the prospective resident. For a long time psychiatry has attracted 8 per cent or 9 per cent of new physicians into psychiatric residencies. This figure apparently has reached 10 per cent in the last year or two, but it is difficult to see how it can go much higher. Yet, if we are to provide enough psychiatrists to take up the increased demand of a rapidly growing population, and to replace those psychiatrists leaving the field each year, we must somehow increase our output, and this seems impossible in the absence of a huge expansion of medical education. In special areas such as child psychiatry, community psychiatry, and public health psychiatry, the prospective shortage is even more serious.

Any manpower planning must explicitly confront these chronic shortages. If we continue to put our major reliance on the illness model of mental disorder, we cannot produce enough of the medical and paramedical people as the model demands. This alone would not be a valid reason for abandoning the illness model, if it were supported firmly by evidence. What I am suggesting is that we are trapped by this model, and that the development of alternative models will lead to new manpower solutions and new institutional solutions whose forms are just now beginning to emerge.

REFERENCES

ALBEE, G. W. 1959. *Mental health manpower trends.* New York: Basic Books.
———. 1963. American psychology in the sixties. *American Psychologist,* 18:90–95.
———. 1967. The relation of conceptual models to manpower needs. In E. L. Cowen, E. A. Gardner, and M. Zax (Eds.), *Emergent approaches to mental health problems.* New York: Appleton-Century-Crofts.
BANDURA, A. 1967. Behavioral psychotherapy. *Scientific American,* 216 (3) :78–86.

BARTON, W. E. 1965. The Second AMA National Congress on Mental Illness and Health. *Mental Hospitals,* 16 (2) :7–10.

BETTELHEIM, B. 1967. *The empty fortress.* New York: The Free Press.

BRUNER, J. 1957. Freud and the image of man. In B. Nelson (Ed.) , *Freud and the 20th century.* Cleveland: Meridian.

CAMERON, D. Problems of health manpower in relation to mental health. Presentation to Consumer Panel National Advisory Commission on Health Manpower, January 5, 1967. (Mimeo.)

DUNHAM, H. W. 1965. Community psychiatry, the newest therapeutic bandwagon. *Archives of General Psychiatry,* 12:303–313.

EYSENCK, H. J. 1957. *The dynamics of anxiety and hysteria.* London: Routledge & Kegan Paul.

FROMM-REICHMANN, F. 1950. *Principles of intensive psychotherapy.* Chicago: University of Chicago Press.

GERARD, R. 1956. Unpublished talk. Committee on Mental Health, Washington, D.C. Quoted by L. G. Abood, A chemical approach to the problem of mental disease. In D. D. Jackson (Ed.) , *The etiology of schizophrenia.* New York: Basic Books. P. 91.

HEATH, R. G. 1960. A biochemical hypothesis on the etiology of schizophrenia. In D. D. Jackson (Ed.) , *The etiology of schizophrenia.* New York: Basic Books.

HERZBERG, F. I. 1966. *Work and the nature of man.* Cleveland: World.

JAHODA, M. 1958. *Current concepts of positive mental health.* New York: Basic Books.

KETY, S. S. 1965. Biochemical theories of schizophrenia. *International Journal of Psychiatry,* 1 (3) :409–430.

MASLOW, A. H. 1954. *Motivation and personality.* New York: Harper.

MILL, J. S. 1863. *On liberty.* (2d ed.) Boston: Ticknor and Fields.

MILTON, O. 1965. Perspectives and trends. In O. Milton (Ed.) , *Behavior disorders: Perspectives and trends.* New York: Lippincott.

National Committee Against Mental Illness. 1966. *What are the facts about mental illness in the United States?* Washington, D.C.: National Committee Against Mental Illness.

RYAN, W. 1967. *Distress in the city: a summary report of the Boston Mental Health Survey (1960–1962).* Boston: Massachusetts Association for Mental Health, Massachusetts Department of Mental Health, and United Community Services of Metropolitan Boston.

SCHEFF, T. J. 1966. *Being mentally ill: a sociological theory.* Chicago: Aldine Publishing Company.

SPENCE, K. W. 1956. *Behavior theory and conditioning.* New Haven: Yale University Press.

ULLMANN, L. P., and L. KRASNER. (Eds.) . 1965. *Case Studies in behavior modification.* New York: Holt, Rinehart, and Winston.

CHAPTER 6

Career Patterns:
Trends and Prospects

PETER H. ROSSI

INTRODUCTION

IN A FREE SOCIETY, individuals to some extent choose
the occupations and jobs they eventually enter and work in: institutions
select among those applicants who present themselves. Models of occupational choice and institutional selection are, therefore, important
considerations in the construction of rational manpower policies. To
change the supply of manpower available to an institutional sector or to
improve the quality of that supply means somehow to motivate individuals of appropriate characteristics and skills to enter upon career-line
patterns that will lead them into the occupations and jobs of that sector.

The social psychology of choice of occupation and job is particularly
important for occupational fields requiring lengthy training periods and
high levels of performance. For example, barring immigration from other
countries, the supply of new physicians entering into practice for the next
eight years is almost completely determined by the number of medical
students, interns, and residents who are presently in medical school and
in the teaching hospitals. A radical rise in the demand for physicians
cannot be met by producing additional doctors for at least the next

decade. Similar but less stringent restrictions apply to the supply of scientists of all sorts, other professionals, and in some degree, even teachers on the elementary and secondary levels.

To the extent that mental health manpower demands are for personnel of high educational attainment and skill levels, planning ahead for the next decade requires actions to be taken now to affect supplies of manpower for the future.

A rational manpower policy is not merely concerned with affecting choice and selection. Highly trained manpower requires educational institutions to train men and women desired. Wages and salary schedules affect changes in supply and particularly the retention of trained individuals within the occupations in question.

This paper is concerned, however, mainly with manpower problems centering around occupational choice. The manpower policy concerns of the past two decades have led to a considerable body of research on the social psychology of occupational choice as it pertains to professional and scientific occupation. Two main types of research have been conducted: "Social bookkeeping" studies mainly concerned with providing descriptive statistics have considerably improved our understanding of the nature of our higher educational "system." More analytically oriented research has provided better understanding about the processes whereby young people choose (and are chosen by) educational institutions and subsequent occupations and jobs.

The purpose of this paper is to review some of the research that has been conducted on the processes of occupational choice among young people and on the prestige of occupations, with a view toward drawing out their implications for manpower policies in the mental health field. As in other fields, research findings and policy implications fit together only loosely. Given a single research finding, there are usually several different policy items that are consonant with the findings. For example, the finding that there is no correlation between the number of children in classes at the elementary and secondary levels and achievement does not necessarily imply a policy of increasing class size, for there are many other reasons why one might prefer small classes over large ones as a matter of policy.[1] For this reason, it is my intention to indicate the range of policies with which the research findings are consonant. Indeed, it appears that empirical research is more useful in providing grounds for rejecting policies than for constructing a uniquely appropriate policy.

PRESTIGE AND RELATED TOPICS

Although the social standing of occupations as a topic for this paper may seem at first glance to be remote from the central problem of recruit-

---

1. It may well be the case that teachers strongly prefer small to large classes, and a policy in favor of small classes may be instituted to maximize teacher satisfaction.

ment, it can easily be shown to be quite closely related. To begin with, the differential evaluation of occupations operates as one of the processes by which individuals are motivated to choose one occupation rather than another. Other things being equal, a more prestigeful occupation may be considered as preferable to a less prestigeful one. Second, occupational groups express a considerable amount of concern with the standings of their occupations. A great deal of effort on the part of some professional associations[2] goes into attempts to improve occupational "images," supposedly on the grounds that such improvements will lead to corresponding gains in ability to attract talented recruits.

Over the past twenty years, and especially in the last three years,[3] a considerable amount of research has been conducted on the prestige standing of occupations. The end results indicated that efforts to change occupational images might best be diverted to endeavors that have a potentially higher payoff. The research findings also have implications for proper strategies for new occupations to employ in fitting themselves into a maximum position in the existing occupational-prestige hierarchy.

The social standing of an occupation can be defined as the popular conception of that occupation's value. The operational definition corresponding to the concept obviously involves some sort of sample survey, in which representative samples of a population are asked to rate occupations. The average ratings given to occupations then constitute measures of their social standing. In a series of studies (Hodge, Siegel, and Rossi, 1966) conducted over the past three years, the National Opinion Research Center (NORC) has obtained such social-standing measures for more than 300 occupations.

The general findings of our studies concerning how occupational groups are regarded present no particular surprises. Professional and scientific occupations, as a group, lead the list, with unskilled and personal-service occupations at the bottom. Among the professions, medicine consistently garners the highest regard. Public administration and business management occupations generally rank below the professions and scientific occupations, although there are specific jobs (e.g., member of the President's Cabinet) that enjoy extremely high average scores.

From the viewpoint of this paper, the general standings of occupations are not as important as some of the properties of these ratings. These are properties that cast considerable doubt on the efficacy of any moves directed at trying to change how particular occupations or occupational groups are evaluated.

2. Indeed, the first national sample survey of the social standings of occupations was conducted by NORC under the auspices of a government agency in the immediate postwar period (1947) out of a concern that scientists were leaving government because of the low prestige enjoyed by government employment.

3. Although the main body of findings has yet to be published, preliminary results can be found in Hodge, Siegel, and Rossi (1966).

The social standings of occupations are invariant over major subgroups of the population. There are little differences between the ratings of occupations given by different regions, class levels, sexes, educational levels, etc. Despite the considerable effort researchers have invested in attempting to find some subgroups of the population that would vary markedly in their evaluations of occupations, none of these efforts has borne fruit. For example, Reiss (1961) reports correlations all above .95 among the sets of average ratings among subgroups identified in the NORC 1947 survey. Svalastoga (1963), in his study of the social standings of occupations in Denmark, notes the same phenomenon. The more recent and more elaborate surveys conducted by NORC in the past few years have yet to find subgroups whose average ratings correlated below 0.9 with any other subgroup or with the average ratings given by the total samples involved. The subgroup variations that do exist amount to expansions or contractions of the set of average scores. Thus, blue-collar workers tend to give ratings that lessen the "distance" among occupations, and white-collar workers tend to give ratings that accomplish just the opposite.

In short, there is a remarkable amount of consensus in the population concerning how occupations should be evaluated.

These ratings are also invariant over differences in the techniques employed to elicit them. Different rating tasks set before respondents produce ratings that are almost identical with those generated by other tasks. For example, it does not matter whether you ask the respondent to rate occupations according to their social standing or to how close to the head of the table they should be placed at a ceremonial dinner (Smith, 1943), or to evaluate their prestige (Counts, 1925) or their contributions to the commonweal, or what have you. All techniques (so far, at least) lead to values that correlate above 0.9 with all other techniques. In short, once respondents are asked to make some evaluations of a relatively large list of occupations, the same evaluations are elicited regardless of the specific form in which the task of evaluation is phrased.

As social research goes, there is a fairly long tradition of research into the prestige positions of occupations. The earliest study was conducted in the 1920's by George S. Counts (1925) and the latest studies by NORC in 1964 and 1965 (Hodge, Siegel, and Rossi, 1966). Comparing occupational titles that have been rated in different studies spaced over that period leads (Hodge, Siegel, and Rossi, 1966) inevitably to the conclusion that very little has changed in the evaluation of occupations over that forty-year period, the correlations between ratings at different points in time all being above 0.9. This stability is especially impressive because the time period involved is one in which there have been considerable changes in the occupational distribution of the labor force. Since the twenties, the United States has experienced a drastic decline in

the number of people in agricultural occupations and a striking increase
in white-collar, professional, and scientific occupations. The implications
for understanding processes of recruitment to occupations are clear:
Since there were no major shifts in the social standings of occupations
over this period, we cannot look to such changes as explanations of
shifts in occupational choices.

Finally, there is considerable evidence that occupations are similarly
rated regardless of the cultural milieu from which the raters are drawn.
Ratings from countries as dissimilar as the Belgian Congo, Ghana, Ja-
pan, the USSR, and the United States show strong similarities, the average correlations among 23 different countries being above 0.9 (Hodge,
Treiman, and Rossi, 1966). Although these high correlations indicate
that there is high intercountry agreement on which are and which are not
prestigeful occupations rather than on the precise position of very specific
occupations (the samples of occupations involved being too small ordinarily to imply anything further), it is noteworthy that the ratings appear to be attached to occupations rather than expressive of cultural
differences representing what one must consider to be a kind of pan-
human understanding of how broad occupational groups stand vis-à-vis
each other.

Given these findings, it seems hardly likely that efforts to change the
social standing of occupations will result in any substantial shifts, or that
these shifts are related to the labor-market positions of occupations. Furthermore, it is quite clear that professional and scientific occupations,
all told, enjoy high reputations, and to the extent that mental health
professions are seen as part of the broad group of professional and scientific occupations, they presently enjoy about as high a level of social
standing in the minds of the general population as one could desire.

Although it is not clear whether there is any significant utility to an
occupational group to enjoy a high social standing, at least as far as recruitment is concerned, there may be an interest in social standing for its
own intrinsic worth.[4] One may conceive of the social standing of an occupation as part of the rewards, however insubstantial, that incumbents
receive by virtue of their occupational role. In this sense there is a
particular problem to be faced by new occupations or new subdivisions
of older occupations. It is instructive in this connection to see how a new

---

4. For example, when young people are asked which occupation they would like
to work at, assuming that they could have any occupation they desired, very few
respond with occupations that are far from what they are likely to enter. Thus, a child
who expects to finish high school but not go on to college responds with occupations
appropriate to high school graduates and rarely indicates that he would like to be a
professional. At the same time, young people tend to give occupations that are slightly
higher than they would ordinarily achieve. These findings indicate that when given a
free choice of this sort, persons tend to choose within the realm of possibility those
occupations that are of higher status (Rivera and Short, 1963).

occupation is fitted into the existing occupational hierarchy. A case in point is provided by the "atomic physicist," an occupation that came into being within the last twenty years and that was studied early in its development in 1947 and more recently in 1963 (Hodge, Siegel, and Rossi, 1966).

Because of the special interest of the sponsoring government agency, the NORC 1947 survey of occupational prestige asked respondents what they thought atomic physicists "did." This question was repeated again concerning this occupation in the NORC replication in 1963, sixteen years and a considerable amount of public attention later. Hodge and Hodge (1966), in their analysis of the two surveys, were able to show that although considerably more people in 1963 were able to rate atomic physicists than in 1947 (55 per cent in 1947 as compared with 26 per cent in 1963 said that they did not know the occupation well enough to rate it), the amount of very specific knowledge about the occupation was not much greater in the later period. In 1947 and in 1963 only 2 per cent to 3 per cent of the respondents gave descriptions of the work done by atomic physicists that could be coded as "correct." The remainder gave vague, partially correct, or totally inaccurate descriptions.

However, qualitative differences between 1947 and 1963 in these descriptions provide a clue to how such new occupations become fitted into the occupational scheme. Although the level of accuracy of the descriptions did not change between 1947 and 1963, respondents in the later survey were much more likely to place atomic physicists as among the scientific occupations. Thus, in 1947 the incidence of bizarre responses was relatively high, e.g., "Studies eggs, doesn't he?" or "Assistant to a physicist," or "He's a spy." In 1963, however, respondents were more likely to place the occupation squarely in the general category of scientific occupations. Incidentally, largely as a consequence of this diffusion of general knowledge concerning the broad occupational grouping to which atomic physicists belong, the social-standing rating of the occupation rose more than that of any other occupation in the period 1947–63.

The implications for the newer occupations that are to make up the health professions of the future are as follows: It will be difficult to diffuse enough specific information about such occupations to produce a broad base of people knowledgeable in detail about such occupations. It should, however, be possible [5] to have such professions seen as part of the general group of highly regarded health care and scientific professions. While I doubt that it is possible to assimilate psychiatric social workers

---

5. Since the social standing of occupations tends to become fixed in individuals in early adolescence, younger children generally showing less agreement with the way in which occupations are rated by adults, a significant point at which to affect the images of such occupations is during this period of development and exploration of the adult world.

into the category of physicians as easily as it is to assimilate psychiatrists into that category, it should be possible to gain some benefit from the association between this occupation and other health care occupations.

The main lesson for mental health manpower policy to be drawn from these findings is that the "image" of an occupation or its "social standing" is yet to be demonstrated as having an important role in recruiting individuals to that occupation. The stability of such "images" or "social standings" over time precludes their behaving as anything more than a constant feature of the occupational landscape. Occupations higher in social standing are viewed as more desirable, but this relatively abstract desirability is apparently much less important than more variable aspects of occupations, to which changes in manpower supply on the labor market are apparently more sensitive.

OCCUPATIONAL CHOICE PROCESSES IN COLLEGE

The major mental health professions necessarily rely on the undergraduate colleges to provide the basic cadres to fill vacancies in their ranks. The decisions made by college students during their undergraduate days and their implementation in postgraduate activities determine to a large extent how many and of what quality will find their ways into this new field. Hence, the study of decision processes during college is directly relevant to the construction of an adequate mental health manpower policy.

The findings related in this section arise mainly out of the surveys of college graduates and graduate students conducted by NORC (Davis, Gottlieb, *et al.*, 1962; Davis, 1964, 1965; Warkov, 1965; Warkov and Zelan, 1965) over the past decade. These studies were based on very large samples of graduating seniors and of graduate students selected from national samples of undergraduate schools and graduate departments. For example, the NORC study of the June, 1961, graduating classes of American colleges was drawn from a sample of 135 schools and comprised 35,000 graduating seniors (Davis, 1964). The NORC study of graduate students in 35 fields registered in 1963 covered 130 graduate schools and more than 20,000 graduate students (Warkov, 1965). In short, these are not parochial studies based upon one or two schools and small numbers of students, but fairly represent the considerable variety of schools and students to be found in the country as a whole.

Popular thinking regards the undergraduate years as those in which the young freshman tries out a variety of disciplines, finally settling as a senior on a career choice that he finds intrinsically interesting and to which his abilities are matched. To some degree popular thinking is correct, but not entirely. The entering freshman ordinarily has a career destination in mind, but he does undergo a period of testing and changing. Table 1 shows the distributions among various categories of anticipated career field as freshmen and seniors. Note that there are gross similarities

Table 1. Freshman and Senior Career Fields: June 1961 Graduating Seniors

	ANTICIPATED	FUTURE CAREERS
	Freshmen	Seniors
Arts and Sciences		
Physical science	6.9%	5.4%
Biological science	1.8	2.1
Social science	2.5	4.0
Humanities and fine arts	6.4	6.5
Professional Fields		
Education	26.9	32.2
Engineering	15.8	8.3
Law	3.7	3.9
Medicine	5.5	2.8
Social work	.4	1.8
Other	17.8	10.3
Other Fields		
Business and administration	12.4	18.2
Agriculture	—[a]	1.5
Fields not on list	—[a]	2.8
100% =	48,993	54,172
No career field or do not expect to work	4,384	901
No answer to question	3,287	1,501
Total weighted N[b]	56,664	56,664

Based upon answers to questions asking seniors to check from a long list of fields the one field which they anticipated as freshmen they would eventually enter and to check the field they anticipated as seniors eventually entering upon.

Adapted from Davis, 1965, Table 2.2, and Davis, 1964, Table 2.2.

[a] Original tables do not break out these categories.

[b] Since students from certain types of schools were systematically underrepresented in the sample (in order to reduce costs of field work), they were given multiple weights in the tabulations. Although approximately 35,000 students answered the questionnaires, through weighting, the N's for tabulations are much larger.

between the two columns. Only about 8 per cent of the seniors had no anticipated careers as freshmen (see numbers at bottom of table) and less than 2 per cent of the seniors anticipated that they would never work.

Some fields are net gainers: biological sciences, social sciences, education, law, social work, and business and administration. Others are net losers: physical sciences, engineering, medicine, and "other professions." The Index of Similarity [6] between the two columns is approximately 17 per cent, indicating that at minimum 17 per cent of the freshmen would

6. Computed by taking the absolute differences between the two columns, summing row by row and dividing by two. Since the two columns do not contain the same number of categories, the application of this index is not entirely appropriate. However, were the categories identical, the Index of Similarity would be of the same magnitude, and hence the present number can serve as a rough approximation.

have to change careers as seniors in order to produce the distribution of career choices as seniors.

The actual proportion of students who change career fields between freshmen and senior years is considerably greater, being close to 50 per cent. Furthermore, considering that this takes into account only the discrepancies between freshmen and senior years and does not *perforce* count changes that may have taken place at other times during the four years of college, 50 per cent change is undoubtedly an underestimation. In other words, more than half of our undergraduates shift career fields at least once during college days.

Perhaps the outstanding feature of Table 1 concerns how strongly oriented toward the educational sector of the economy are June 1961 graduates. Almost one out of every three graduates is headed for a career in elementary and secondary schools (the former being a particularly frequent goal for the 40 per cent of the graduates who are women). Another large proportion of those headed for arts and sciences careers intends to pursue them within the context of higher educational institutions. All told, half or more of the graduates are aiming for one level or another of our layered educational system.

Another large group has elected careers in business. It is important to keep in mind that the career field "business" in Table 1 represents mainly those who seek careers as business managers and administrators directly: There are a large number of additional college graduates who will end up in the private sector working for private corporations as chemists, physicists, market research analysts, lawyers, etc., but who do not show up in this table as choosing business as a career, because they are more oriented toward their future occupation than toward the setting in which that occupation is to be pursued.

Note further that the future cadres of mental health professionals cannot be directly counted in Table 1. Some unknown proportion of the future physicians will be psychiatrists, some of the social scientists will turn out to be clinical psychologists, and some of the social workers will either be psychiatric social workers or work within a mental health context. To become a mental health professional in this historical period is a process of choosing the context in which one will pursue a profession and a content area in which one will exercise a particular type of professional expertise. "Mental health professional" (with the possible exception of psychiatrist and psychiatric social worker) is not yet an occupational goal recognized and striven for as such at the level of professional development that characterizes undergraduates. The choice of a mental health career comes later in the stages of professional development, most likely sometime during the post-graduate training that most of the graduates will pursue.[7]

---

7. At time of graduation, three out of every four graduating seniors anticipated

In short, the mental health-career pipelines are filled by tapping into the larger trunklines leading to the major professions and scientific careers. To get more mental health professionals can be accomplished in two ways: (1) filling up the trunklines leading to the professional groupings from which mental health professionals are recruited; (2) persuading those in the major professional groupings to seek the practice of their profession within mental health contexts.

Over the past two decades, considerable increases have been experienced in the growth of the professional component of the mental health sector of our economy. In part this has been the result of strengthening the educational system concerned with training professional mental health personnel, i.e., enlarging programs for the training of psychiatrists, psychiatric social workers, and clinical psychologists, and in part by attracting persons already professionally trained to enter mental health professional roles. The extent to which this has been accomplished by weakening the supply of personnel available to other fields is hard to estimate, but certainly the personnel must have come from other lines in the occupational roster.[8]

As one could anticipate from Table 1, the various career fields show considerable variations one from the other in their ability both to retain students who initially chose them as freshmen and to recruit students from other fields. Table 2 contains "turnover" data on the career fields shown in Table 1. Note particularly that there are two indexes that bear special attention. Row B (proportion of freshmen who "transition out") is an index that measures the ability of a field to retain those who initially chose it—the higher the index, the lower the field's ability in this regard. Row E ("transition in") is a measure of a field's ability to attract

---

taking some kind of postgraduate training at some time or other, with one out of three intending to enter upon such training the year following graduation. Obviously, the proportion entering upon postgraduate training varied widely with fields: Almost everyone intending to go into medicine was entering medical school the year following graduation, while few of those with business administration career intentions intended to enter graduate schools of business immediately.

8. Whether any other fields have been slighted is a very complicated matter to determine. For example, the largest component of occupational aspiration of college graduates is the field of elementary and secondary education. This is a field that could compensate a great deal for a reduced supply of recruits by making better use of persons already trained—for example, women who have taught for a few years and then dropped out of the labor force to rear their children. Similarly, a reduction in the supply of physicians going into general practice can be compensated for by an increase in the efficiency of medical care, so that the same number of doctors could treat a large number of persons at the same level of quality, perhaps through the use of better drugs, group practice, etc. If persons going into the mental health professions are primarily being recruited from fields that are growing in efficiency to a degree that compensates for the loss of personnel, then it would be hard to say that such fields were being depleted of their recruits. In other words, differential recruitment of personnel among the various professional fields can hardly be said to be entirely competitive in the sense of a zero sum game.

Table 2. Turnover by Career Fields

TURNOVER		Education	Business	Social sciences	Humanities	Biological sciences	Other Professions	Law	Physical sciences	Medicine	Engineering
Proportion of freshmen choices	A	0.253	0.116	0.023	0.059	0.017	0.169	0.034	0.065	0.053	0.148
Transition out	B	0.152	0.274	0.642	0.503	0.584	0.427	0.437	0.493	0.565	0.487
Loss (AxB)	C	0.038	0.032	0.015	0.030	0.010	0.072	0.015	0.032	0.030	0.072
Proportion not in field as freshmen (1.00-A)	D	0.747	0.884	0.977	0.941	0.983	0.831	0.966	0.935	0.947	0.852
Transition in	E	0.158	0.098	0.027	0.039	0.015	0.075	0.021	0.025	0.008	0.013
Gain (DxE)	F	0.118	0.086	0.026	0.037	0.013	0.062	0.020	0.023	0.008	0.011
Net change (F-C)	G	+0.080	+0.054	+0.011	+0.007	+0.003	—0.010	+0.005	—0.009	—0.022	—0.061
Per cent change (G/A)	H	+32	+47	+48	+12	+18	—06	+15	—14	—42	—41
Recruits as per cent of defectors		306	275	184	124	151	86	136	74	24	16

N
NA Freshmen only   49,817
NA Seniors only   2,834
NA Both   3,560
                       453
Total weighted N   56,664

recruits from other fields—the higher the index, the more attractive the field to recruits.

Fields can be roughly characterized as "gainers," those with high gains, low losses, and net increases (business and education); "losers," those with high losses and low gains (medicine, engineering, the physical sciences, and "other professions"); and "traders" (social sciences, biological sciences, law, and the humanities), those with high loss and recruitment rates that compensate for the losses.

It should be borne in mind that while these numbers, when expressed as proportions, appear to be relatively small, when considered in terms of the absolute numbers of undergraduates involved, relatively large-scale shifts are being registered. For example, the 1961 graduating class is estimated to have been 350,000, of whom 19,250 looked forward to medicine as a career when they were freshmen, that number dropping to 9,800 as seniors. In other words, shifts in the transition probabilities in the second and third place could lead to considerable fluctuations in the supply of students available for pursuing particular career lines.

If we probe further into the kinds of students who shift fields, we find that there are several characteristics that predict movement into and out of different fields: the academic performance of students, sex, the kinds of occupational values they hold, and their socioeconomic status. Several generalizations, although not without exception, can be made:

1. Fields demanding high performance from students tend to lose during college without gaining many new recruits, e.g., medicine, physical sciences, and engineering. The major exception to this generalization is the humanities, which tends both to retain high-performing students and to attract additional recruits.

2. Fields demanding high performance tend to lose women and retain men, even though women, on the whole, have better performance records than men. Exception: the social sciences (which are not highly demanding) become more predominantly masculine.

3. Students holding occupational values [9] at variance with their occupational choice tend to move out of a career field and into more

9. The analytical utility of occupational values is somewhat in question. Davis (1964), Holland (1966), and Rosenberg (1960) found asking students what kinds of things they would like to achieve in their occupational choices a useful predictor of the choice; but it is not clear how much additional understanding is achieved by finding out that students who want to be doctors are likely to say that they would enjoy working with people, while mechanical engineers are likely to say that they like to work with things. It is not established that occupational values are long enduring characteristics of individuals that guide their choices of occupations or the contrary, that values represent a rationalization of choices initially made out of other considerations. Without additional research on how occupational values come about, and their enduring quality over time, we are somewhat at a loss to interpret their analytical significance. A recent unpublished dissertation (Underhill, 1967) analyzing the relationships between changes in occupational values and occupational choices in the

congenial career fields. The relevant value patterns are "working with people," "being original and creative," "desire for money," and "working with things."

4. Students coming from high socioeconomic status backgrounds are more likely to remain in some career fields, e.g., law and medicine, or to be recruited into others, e.g., social science and the humanities, although by and large socioeconomic background is not a strong predictor of career-choice shifts.

The undergraduate educational experience then appears to be one in which the student enters with some sort of long-range career choice, tests that choice against his ability to successfully complete the appropriate curriculum and against the image of the career choices implicit in the curriculum, and adjusts his choice accordingly. As seniors, undergraduates hold choices that are more consistent with their abilities and interests than they held as freshmen. It is important, however, to stress that this is best characterized as a strain toward consistency rather than a situation in which students and career choices are matched perfectly. This is so because of three reasons: First, some fields present less of a consistent set of ability and interest demands and, hence, can be attractive to a wide variety of students, e.g., education and the social sciences. Second, our understanding and measurement of relevant student characteristics are far from perfect. Third, we can anticipate that the students' perceptions of their abilities, interests, and the relevant characteristics of fields are also far from perfect. In short, there is enough looseness in the system to insure that every field gets some proportion of talented and motivated individuals and some proportion of students with deficiencies in both. The differences among fields represent differences in the mixes of students rather than clear-cut typological distinctions.

IMPLICATIONS FOR MENTAL HEALTH MANPOWER

The major characteristics of the mental health professions that must be borne in mind as we try to assess the meaning of these findings for manpower policy are that they are derivatives of the major professional groups toward which college students appear to be headed. In other words, there are few undergraduates who are directly headed for mental health professions: Instead, they are headed for more inclusive professional groups, of which the mental health professions are a part. The mental health jobs of the future will be filled by college students who are aiming in their general direction rather than pursuing a direct career line with mental health as a specific destination.

---

postgraduate period has found that the pattern is quite complete. For some fields, particularly the more demanding ones, individuals choosing them tend to change their values over time to fit their choices, while in the "softer," less demanding fields, the opposite pattern holds.

Perhaps the first strategy that ought to be considered is one that sets up the mental health professions as a primary career line of its own. This means divorcing psychiatry from medicine, clinical psychology from academic psychology, and psychiatric social work from social work. Assuming for the moment that such a move would be politically possible—that medicine would allow psychiatry to depart, etc.—what would be gained from such a move and what would be lost? The major gain would be the establishment of a direct appeal to undergraduates (assuming that the mental health training institution would be mainly postgraduate) and a labor supply that would be more responsive, for that reason, to shifts in demand. One could expect that among undergraduate career aspirations would appear new categories corresponding to the specific mental health occupations for which the new postgraduate institutions were preparing.

The losses to be sustained from such a change would depend largely on where the new professions would fit into the existing hierarchy of occupations. Note that the occupations that are characterized by high losses during undergraduate education are also those characterized by high demands for performance and by relatively rigid undergraduate curriculum. Thus, premedical training requires high performance of students and training in the basic sciences. Physics apparently requires more in the way of a curriculum, but not necessarily as uniformly high a level of performance. Would the new mental health professions, as a separate occupational grouping, be more like medicine and physics or more like education, business, and the social sciences—more tolerant about performance and curriculum?

Given the fact that the present mental health professions recruit from a variety of fields with varying levels of demanded performance and undergraduate preparation, it would seem to me that a move in this direction would place the mental health careers in the same league with education and the social sciences, attractive to a broad range of talent and a field to which one could always turn when other aspirations turn out to be unsuitable.

It is not easy to weigh the relative advantages versus the disadvantages of such a move. Did the fields of elementary and secondary education gain or lose by becoming separate from the substantive disciplines? One suspects they gained a larger and more flexible manpower pool but lost in stature and expertise.

Another broad strategy is to leave the system as it is but expend efforts at two points: (1) increase the number of individuals going through the total educational system on the general ground that the more the major trunk lines are filled, the more can be siphoned off at the peripheral branches; (2) increase efforts at the postgraduate level to divert manpower into mental health contexts. This is apparently the policy that is being pursued at the moment, with special attention given to the second rather than the first point of leverage.

The first point of leverage is clearly to raise the number of young people seeking undergraduate training and subsequently graduate training. It is difficult to see that the rate of college enrollment can be increased faster than has been the case in the last two decades.[10] The demographic structure of the present American population is sufficiently favorable to guarantee this increase without a shift in the rate of enrollment, at least for the next decade. While some additional effort might be profitably expended to make sure that the rate among highly talented high school graduates is maintained and possibly increased, the reservoir of college graduates will be replenished and filled adequately during the next decade.

The efforts expended at points beyond college graduation in attracting to the mental health fields persons who have been aiming at more general professional and scientific callings boil down to two main efforts: (1) fellowship and scholarship support for persons in such groups; (2) research funds for work directly in mental health or closely related fields that serve to induce a certain visibility to the mental health field within graduate and professional schools and departments.

Although it is extremely difficult to assess the effectiveness of fellowships and scholarships in shifting about the attention of graduate and professional students to one or another topic, it is certainly apparent from NORC research (Davis *et al.*, 1962; Warkov, 1965) that such programs hardly affect the distribution of students among broad career fields. For example, at the moment the biological sciences are among the best supported of all major career fields. The worst graduate student in biology has a higher probability of holding a stipend than the best student in the humanities. Yet, the academic quality of humanities' graduate students is, on the average, better than that of students in the biological sciences. Or, medical students are among the most poorly supported (judged in terms of stipends), yet, as a group, they rank the highest in terms of their academic performance as undergraduates. Nor does it seem to be the case that appreciable numbers of potential graduate and professional students are deterred from pursuing postgraduate study by

---

10. Incidentally, there is some evidence (Davis, 1963) that the rate of attendance at college, once high school graduation has been achieved, has not changed substantially over the past 40 years. The proportion of youths finishing high school has substantially changed, however, leading to a greater number of students attending college. Hence, the main leverage point in the supply of students for undergraduate training has been the high school. This is not to say that significant increases in the proportion of high school graduates who go on to college cannot be achieved; it is merely to say that the increase in college attendance, up to this point, has been a function more of the greater rates of high school graduation than of the greater rates of college-going among high school graduates.

the lack of financial support. In 1963 (Warkov, 1965), the average graduate and professional student had household and educational expenses of approximately $4,000 per year. While the amount did not vary from field to field, the sources of his funds did: in fields with low levels of stipend support, funds were obtained from part-time work and the contributions of wives and families; in fields with high stipend support, stipends constituted the major source of funds.

Whatever effects graduate fellowship and scholarship policies may have, they appear to be mainly in directing attention to particular sub-areas of study and research rather than in affecting the numbers of students entering broad fields. Thus, the saturation of clinical psychology and biology with stipends for graduate study apparently does not affect the number of people going into those fields, but it might affect the kinds of work they will pursue as graduate students and the kinds of contexts in which they will employ the skills they acquire while in school.

If this analysis has any merit, then a good argument can be made for not saturating an entire field with stipend support in order to obtain more personnel for a subfield thereof, but rather selectively employing stipends to influence study plans, dissertation research, and hence subsequent employment. Thus, it may be better to give out NIMH stipends to only a small proportion of clinical psychologists, tying the stipends directly into study within mental health contexts (e.g., hospitals, clinics, etc.) or into dissertation research on topics directly relevant to mental health concerns. The present practice of supporting large proportions of clinical psychologists without regard to specific occupational goals and curriculum may be doing a great deal of good for clinical psychology as a field but might be wasteful as far as producing clinical psychologists who will be working within directly relevant mental health contexts.[11]

There can be little doubt that the availability of funds for research in particular areas has affected the distribution of activities and concerns of researchers. For example, within the field of sociology, the rise of medical sociology as a specialty over the past two decades is a tribute to the research funds made available by the various National Health Institutes. Similarly, the newly found (or rather rediscovered) interest in the poor and the disadvantaged is a function of the funds made available through the Office of Economic Opportunity, the Department of Labor, and the

---

11. In specific terms, training grants to departments of psychology may be wasteful, because departments are less selective in awarding traineeships than the fellowships given out directly by NIMH, in which some central surveillance can be given to the course of study, types of internships, and areas of dissertation research pursued by the student. In an effort not to be too restrictive on the academic autonomy of departments and universities, NIMH may have allowed itself to be exploited, however benignly, by departments interested primarily in obtaining support for students entering a wider range of subfields than encompassed by the direct interests of the mental health field.

Office of Education. To the extent that researchers working on the problems of mental health are to be counted as mental health personnel, then research funds undoubtedly do affect the size of a component of the scientific and professional labor force.

That the availability of funds can affect the distribution of other types of personnel can be seen very dramatically in the case of the Poverty Program. A professionally trained cadre for the Poverty Program was attracted within a very short period of time. Whether the personnel who came were optimally trained for their jobs is an open question. Well-paying jobs can attract applicants, retain personnel in a field, and provide incentives for persons to prepare for those fields. Indeed, the growth of the mental health professional field over the past two decades is a dramatic witness to the efficacy of this process.

However, personnel per se is not the only objective of a manpower policy. A rational manpower policy seeks to provide an adequate supply of appropriately trained personnel with the requisite amount of ability to employ that training effectively. Obtaining psychiatrists, psychiatric social workers, and clinical psychologists with good training and high ability levels requires in large part operating on the processes by which young persons enter upon educational experiences that will lead them into the proper occupations and jobs. This means working on undergraduate and graduate populations in the case ·of professional mental health workers to affect the ways in which their choices are made. It also implies that a rational manpower policy should have a long-term perspective, being concerned as much with the personnel supplies of the next decade as it is with whether the vacancies of today are filled.

CONCLUSIONS

The main argument of this paper has been that a policy for increasing the supplies of adequately trained mental health manpower has had, almost of necessity, to be an indirect policy. Because mental health manpower on the professional level is derived from larger professional groups, it is difficult to affect at early stages the number of students headed directly for mental health professions. The career decisions made by young people are in terms of broad occupational groupings rather than specific jobs in specific contexts. Hence, manpower policy has had to be directed at recruiting against the competition of other specific jobs among persons who have already been attracted to some general profession.

Under these circumstances, a mental health manpower policy has to be relatively inefficient, relying mainly on the thesis that whatever benefits the broad professional groupings from among which mental health professionals are recruited will eventually affect the supply. Short of establishing a new professional grouping, with all attendant dangers, there does not seem to be a more efficient way of proceeding.

REFERENCES

COUNTS, G. S. 1925. The social status of occupations: a problem in vocational guidance. *School Review,* 33:16–27.

DAVIS, J. A. 1963. Higher education: selection and opportunity. *School Review,* 71:249–265.

———. 1964. *Great aspirations: the graduate school plans of America's college seniors.* Chicago: Aldine Publishing Company.

———. 1965. *Undergraduate career decisions: correlates of occupational choice.* Chicago: Aldine Publishing Company.

———, D. GOTTLIEB, et al. 1962. *Stipends and spouses: the finances of American arts and science graduate students.* Chicago: University of Chicago Press.

HODGE, R. W., and P. HODGE. 1966. Whatever happened to the atomic physicist? Chicago: National Opinion Research Center. (Mimeo.)

———, P. M. SIEGEL, and P. H. ROSSI. 1966. Occupational prestige in the United States: 1925–1963. In R. Bendix and S. M. Lipset (Eds.), *Class, status, and power.* New York: Free Press of Glencoe.

———, D. J. TREIMAN, and P. H. ROSSI. 1966. A comparative study of occupational prestige. In R. Bendix and S. M. Lipset (Eds.), *Class, status, and power.* New York: Free Press of Glencoe.

HOLLAND, J. L. 1966. *The psychology of vocational choice.* Waltham, Mass.: Blaisdell.

REISS, A. J., O. D. DUNCAN, P. K. HATT, and C. C. NORTH. 1962. *Occupations and social status.* New York: Free Press of Glencoe.

RIVERA, R., and J. F. SHORT. 1963. Occupational goals: A comparative analysis. Paper presented at the meeting of the Society for the Study of Social Problems.

ROSENBERG, M., E. A. SUCHMAN, and R. K. GOLDSEN. 1957. *Occupations and values.* Glencoe, Ill.: Free Press.

SMITH, M. 1943. An empirical scale of prestige status of occupations. *American Sociological Review,* 8:185–192.

SVALASTOGA, K. 1959. *Prestige, class, and mobility.* Copenhagen: Glydendal.

UNDERHILL, R. 1967. *Occupational values and post-college career change.* (Doctoral dissertation, University of Chicago.) Chicago: University Microfilms. No. 20146.

WARKOV, S. 1965. Graduate student finances. Report #103. Chicago: NORC. (Mimeo.)

———, and J. ZELAN. 1965. *Lawyers in the making.* Chicago: Aldine Publishing Company.

CHAPTER 7

Individual Motivation and Personal Factors in Career Choice

ANNE ROE

T HE TERM "CAREER CHOICE" may give the impression that at some precise and specifiable moment or moments, one decides, more or less rationally, to undertake a particular vocation. Although this may appear to have happened occasionally, to proceed on any assumption that this is usual is to obscure the complex and multi-determined nature of occupational histories. The job histories of most men in our society and of an increasing number of women provide a more meaningful clue to their personal histories and to the kinds of people they are than any other separable aspect of their lives. I shall, therefore, be discussing career as a particular way in which to view a life history. The term career carries with it the implication of a professional or semiprofessional occupation following a more or less well-established pattern. This is appropriate in the context of this conference but is not for occupational histories in general.

Although I shall concentrate on factors immediate to the individual (not necessarily or even in large part under his control), it is important to keep clearly in mind that these factors operate within a societal context, and that the precise nature of this context at any point in time sets very decided limits within which personal variables may operate.[1] We are an industrialized society with as highly differentiated an occupational structure as the world has yet seen. This could lead to the expectation that in such a society there should be an appropriate occupation for any individual, whatever his capacities or desires, as well as enough appropriate people to fill any needs of the society. Unfortunately, this is not the case. The unmet social need into which we are inquiring is only an example of many others. That the most important of these needs are also in the public sector of the economy should not be forgotten; in itself it is a clue to the extent and nature of the social changes we are experiencing.

That we are an industrialized society sets up such a plethora of career possibilities that one might expect sober contemplation of them to induce only a state of galloping indecision. It probably would, but no individual ever does contemplate all of them. Imagine going through the *Dictionary of Occupational Titles* (U.S. Labor Dept., 1965), or even the *Occupational Outlook Handbook* (U.S. Labor Dept., 1965), page by page to see what the possibilities might be. (Bad enough to go through the OOH page by page just to classify the occupations!) Quite apart from the severe limitations imposed by ignorance, social restrictions of a variety of sorts are operating. The most pervasive general one is the overall state of the economy related to the issues of peace or war, inflation or depression. There may be more jobs than takers, with corresponding changes in requirements and new chances for women or Negroes owing to less stringent educational or training requirements. On the other hand, in certain areas, conditions may be just the opposite or any stage in-between. Although the national situation affects all localities, there are local situations that additionally restrict or open possibilities for individual members of certain subgroups in the population. We sometimes forget that statistics on these matters are compiled from data on individuals and we may often fail to see their significance for individual persons. (See, for example, my comments on Ginzberg's *Life Styles of Educated Women* [Roe, 1966].)

Within these more general limitations are those relevant to the position of the family into which any individual is born. The effects here include the whole socioeconomic complex in which the family is embedded and that particular family's place in it. Some of these effects, such as those related to minority position, are almost too obvious to mention, but even

---

1. I am assuming that Dr. Rossi and others will discuss such issues as prestige scales and changes in occupational patterns, including sex and race, but I shall also mention them briefly in order to place my discussion into a general background.

here the total position is seldom the result of that one aspect alone. There are, for example, Negro families who are not poverty-stricken and who have intellectual and cultural standards as high as any others, and for whose children the fact of race is less crippling than are the ignorance and stupidity of many white families. But, even at best in America, in any equation expressing probabilities of action or choice, the symbol for race never has a coefficient of zero.

Again, family income is an obviously restricting factor—and at both ends of the scale—but it is less important in some situations than in others. For example, the scion of a well-known but now impoverished New England family is in a totally different position from that of the son of a struggling immigrant family, and is in some ways much more favorably situated than the son of a newly rich man. It seems clear that neither money nor social position of parents is as important a factor in occupational histories as are the family values. A child from a family that places a high value on education is more likely to get an advanced education than one from another family of equal or greater income for whom education is unimportant, or even undesirable. Even that is a great oversimplification, since one family may value an education for its economic advantage, and another for its enrichment of life. And, incidentally, the colleges selected for the sons seem to vary rather consistently with this. To carry it further, success in college or graduate school may depend to some degree upon the match between family and college values, for of course colleges vary in value emphases, too. I noted that limitations are imposed at both ends of a socioeconomic scale, although they may be more stringent at the lower ends. But surely it is obvious that pressures to live up to high intellectual or cultural standards may fall very heavily upon ungifted children. It is probably harder for the son of a Harvard professor to become a mechanic, even if he would like to be one, than it is for the son of a mechanic to become a Harvard professor. Sons of famous men can be in a very uncomfortable position indeed. The longer I study occupations and people in them, the more I find that even without considering interpersonal relations within the family, the influence of family background is pervasive and subtle beyond any analyses we have yet achieved.

The only factor that is as continuing and pervasive an influence as the socioeconomic one is sex. Again, there is more to the situation than such obvious facts as that the occupational histories of women are very different from those of men, that their significance in the total life picture is usually very different, and that the percentages of men and women in the same occupation are likely to be very different. It has been the thesis of many authors—chiefly women—that the fact that some occupations are extremely difficult for women to enter, however adequate their talents and training, has been brought about by the selfish intention of a dominant group to maintain a fancied superiority. Without denying in the least that such a situation has been and continues to be a factor (just as it is a large factor in the present civil rights struggle), it is my personal opinion that the present sex division of labor in our occupational structure has developed with as much rationality as irrationality. This is not to say that as our understanding of men and women and their differences increases, we should not also promote changes in the occupational patterns in society. Any studies of aptitudes of men and women show such overlapping that distinctions based on these are ridiculous. On the other hand, values and interests do not overlap to the same extent; even the factorial structures may be different, and whether culturally or biologically induced, such differences appear in the earliest years and persist throughout life. These differences have been important elements in the development of the occupational structure, and we should exploit, rather than deny or deprecate, them.

An occupational history is determined for the individual, not only by the factors mentioned above, but also by his individual life experiences, beginning with his birth. The things that engage his attention, his ways of relating to others, and the extent to which his genetic capacities are realized are all interaction products, and all affect directly or indirectly how he comes to spend his life. To account for any life history, we need to know something of these, and also to trace such decision points as are determinable and such chance factors as may intervene. Never underestimate the role of chance, or, in giving it its due, forget that the reaction to that chance is an individual matter.

In the rest of this paper I shall try to give you such information as is available on what kinds of people follow the occupations with which we are concerned and how they come to do it.[2] And though information is sparse, it is more than could be gained were we to try to learn something about those who are more or less successful. It may be useful to consider the evidence from two points of view—what makes the occupations attractive, i.e., their pulling power, and what impels people toward them, the individual push into them.

Our task is easier, not only because we have few occupations to consider, but also because most of them have in common the requirement of a period of special training, and to get to this involves some degree of long-range planning. It also follows that, once through the training, there

---

2. I have looked for material on psychiatrists, clinical and counseling psychologists, psychiatric nurses, social workers, occupational therapists, and psychiatric aides, but I cannot claim an exhaustive search of the literature for any of these. Where several references have contained essentially similar material, I have not, as a rule, included more than one. For all these groups, however, it has been necessary to look into data on the more general professions, i.e., medicine, psychology, nursing, and so on, since there is very little indeed on the specialty groups and, in most cases, the decision is first to become a physician or a nurse, and later a specialty is chosen.

is relatively little likelihood of leaving the occupation, both because by then the individual has a very good idea of what is involved and how he likes it, and because so much time and money have been invested that choosing a different occupation would require very strong motivation indeed. Such considerations, however, hardly apply to one group, psychiatric aides, and they may not apply to new job categories as these are developed.

What are the things about these occupations that make them attractive? Physicians always appear at or very near the top in any list of the prestige of occupations. The physician is the "hero" of the American college student, as O'Dowd and Beardslee (1960) put it. Any list of occupations chosen by elementary or high school pupils also finds the physician chosen by many more pupils than will ever enter the field of medicine. This is true of most of the professions; they are highly visible, and the rewards in terms of respect, independence of action and authority, not to mention income, seem to be well understood. Part of this respect has depended upon a belief in the selflessness of physicians—a belief the AMA has pretty effectively undermined. Within the total group of medical specialties, however, the psychiatrist does not rank high, in spite of his average income. I think this has to do with psychiatry's deemphasis on the natural sciences. In one respect, this high prestige-ranking of the physician is anomalous; the physician combines two quite different sets of values (as does the nurse, perhaps to a lesser extent)—the theoretical and intellectual values of scientific interests, and the social values of those who care for others. Now, caring for others is considered a strongly female attribute, and such attributes are not generally given high regard in male activities in our culture. No doubt the scientific aspect helps take the curse off this, but, in addition, it has occurred to me to wonder whether the assumption of absolute authority, and the sometimes rather rigid expressions of this in regard to those in the other occupations we are considering, may not have a defensive basis. In spite of the strong social values of this profession, only about 7 per cent of our physicians are women. Women constitute a somewhat higher proportion in psychiatry (12 per cent), but this is still rather low.

Clinical and counseling psychologists, like psychiatrists, rate lower within their professional specialty groups than the more strictly experimentally oriented specialists, and in many other respects the relationships are similar. There are, however, relatively more women among clinical psychologists than in some other specialties.

Nursing rates high among women's occupations and is strongly stereotyped as a female occupation (only about one tenth of the registered nurses in the country are male). It does, however, include some admixture of science interests (see, e.g., Triggs, 1947). As the field has developed in recent years, it has changed considerably from intimate bedside care to increased emphasis on technical and managerial functions (except for private-duty nurses). I do not know of any prestige scales for nursing specialties, or whether there is any income differential. Nursing has certainly lost a considerable amount of its "pulling power" for modern youth, in part because of the relatively low-income scale in relation to training time. I think, too, there may be some subtle appreciation of the present conflicting ideals in nursing; somehow it does not seem quite so straightforwardly care-taking as it used to.

Social work, long tabbed as a woman's occupation, has shown a remarkable change in this respect since the war. In many of the schools of social work today the student body is 40 per cent or more male. It is also true that within the profession, men advance more rapidly and more frequently to administrative positions. The contrast with nursing in terms of sex ratio is very great and I do not fully understand the reasons, except that in the hospital situation the authority relations between physician and nurse may be more easily maintained if the nurse is a woman. Physician and social worker in a general hospital are much less closely associated, although in most psychiatric hospitals and clinics the association is a close one. Some of the influx of men into social work can be explained by the GI Bill, which made possible an advanced education. Among the small group of male social workers I studied, there were several whose move into social work was directly stimulated by wartime experiences: the discovery that they could be personally helpful to others and could derive satisfaction from this. For example, two men who had been pharmacists' mates in the navy were both, for considerable periods, the closest approximation to medical care available to their companions, and found that they were being asked for and giving psychological help as well. There was another, a bombardier, a devoutly religious man, whose concern for the souls of his crewmates in imminent danger of death became transferred to concern for their earthly welfare. Note that these experiences occurred within a highly masculine setting.

Occupational therapy is one of the less well-known specialties, and is another field whose technical content has changed considerably over the years. There are only some 8,000 occupational therapists, and I should think that women predominate. With the increasing use of rehabilitative workshops, this situation too may change.

Finally we come to the psychiatric aide, lowest in the pecking order and, in most psychiatric hospitals, the person who has the most contact with patients (an interesting negative correlation). The attraction of this occupation has little to do with prestige or income but is mostly dependent, I suspect, upon its availability to minority-group members and those with relatively little education. I think that considerably more attention should be paid to this group. They are in a most strategic position and, with appropriate additional training, could not only make greater contributions, but also derive more personal satisfaction from their work.[3]

So much for the pulling power of these occupations. They all have in common (or should have) a particular aim: the alleviation of psychological distress. They should, therefore, exert the greatest attraction for persons for whom nurturance and caring for others is a particularly satisfying form of behavior. Their demands in this respect are very neatly summed up in the new U.S. Employment Service occupational classification. This assigns to each occupation a 6-digit code, the last 3 digits of which have to do with the level of functions required with regard to skills in handling Data, People, and Things. The lower the digit assigned, the higher the skills required, and 8, the largest digit used, means that those skills are irrelevant. For these occupations the codes are:

	D	P	T
Psychiatrist	1	o	8
Clinical psychologist	1	o	8
Psychiatric nurse [4]	–	–	–
Psychiatric social worker	1	o	8
Psychiatric occupational therapist [4]	–	–	–
Psychiatric aide	8	7	8
Physician	1	o	1
Experimental psychologist	o	8	8
Registered nurse	3	7	8
Social worker	1	o	8
Occupational therapist	1	2	8

Note the very low ratings for aide and the RN for interpersonal skills!

In my own classification of occupations (Roe, 1956), all of the above belong in the same group, one made up of occupations whose primary focus is on close interpersonal relations of a succoring or nurturant sort. Within this grouping, however, the level, or degree, of interpersonal relations involved differs over a considerable range.

Barker (1964) has reported an inverse correlational analysis of mean semantic differential ratings toward twenty types of disability in order to describe the degree of resemblance of public concepts toward such conditions as alcoholism, tuberculosis, congenital blindness, psychosis, etc. He found two very distinct and contrasting attitudinal factors, one concerning organic disabilities, the other concerning functional ones. Although this is, of course, an analysis of the perception of relationships among disabilities, it does suggest that the semantic differential might be used to discover persons for whom one or the other type of disorder is less repellent, or to investigate changes in such perceptions with training

---

3. I remember being very much impressed some years ago at the training initiated for them at Fort Lyons VA Hospital.

4. Not available.

experiences. Possibly such an approach might be useful to select persons to work with particular types or kinds of illness or conditions.

The greatest number of studies of personnel have utilized students as subjects. This detracts considerably from their maximum usefulness; but, since in all but the aide group one must go through highly specialized training, student studies are not without value. In general, the overall findings across fields is analogous to that reported by Cooley (1963) for scientists: the pool of potential scientists (as defined by occupational choice) grew steadily smaller from fifth grade to graduate school, but those who did remain in science were almost always in the earlier pools. Movement was out of, not into, the group. *The moral, for us, would seem to be that any effort at redirecting choices should start in the early years, and continue to be developed.*

In the following sections I will try to bring together for each specialty what is known about characteristics of those in the field and their personal histories and reasons for selecting that field. The evidence, however, is not only sparse; some of it is contradictory. In general it seems true that intellectual abilities and aptitudes have shown much less differentiation than have values and interests. There does seem to be a quite early differentiation into two distinct foci of interest—on persons or not on persons. Person interest is more prevalent as a dominant focus in women than in men. This can develop on either of two bases: interpersonal relationships can have given the greatest pleasure and have been the most significant experiences, so that they are naturally sought for; or they can have introduced strain in such a way that satisfaction has not been attained but the search for it is continued. Alternatively, of course, one may turn away from them and concentrate on non-persons, but this approach can also be entirely nondefensive. I am of the opinion that whether the attitude is primarily defensive or not is a major determinant of differences in the style of its expression within the same activities. (A pity that the Luborsky and Holt [1957] studies of psychotherapists in training did not include appropriate data on this point.)

There are some differences related to age in the ultimate determination of occupational choice among these fields, but these are largely a function of knowledge about the field and contact with it—personal contact, that is not just classroom reports. So, selection of psychology or occupational therapy comes later than may selection of medicine (70 per cent choose before age 16) or nursing (60 per cent choose before age 16). In the mental health subfields, selection may be still later, although not necessarily so.

Psychotherapists

Funkenstein (1965) has observed that students entering medical school intending to specialize in psychiatry are more likely to have higher verbal than quantitative skills and to find the first two years extremely difficult. On the other hand, the "student scientist" with considerable quantitative aptitude finds the first two years much more palatable than the later ones, which have greater clinical emphasis. Kelly and Goldberg (1959) noted that therapists among psychologists were likely to have had difficulty with mathematics and science in high school.

For male medical students in general, the most striking and consistent difference from other students on the MMPI was reported by Schofield (1953) to be their elevation on the Mf scale—that is, toward the feminine side, which is consistent with the earlier remarks on sex stereotyping in occupations. (Results on female medical students are not reported: I would expect them to be just the opposite.) The total profiles, however, did not suggest any basic personality pattern that would distinguish medical students from other college students. The most characteristic feature of Rorschachs of psychologists is their interest in persons, and clinicians show this even more strongly than other psychologists.

Eron (1954) has reported that the Rorschach is generally of no value in selecting medical students. The extensive work of Luborsky and Holt (1957) with psychiatrists in training, and the studies of Abel and her coworkers (1956) on selection of psychotherapists for training (both psychiatrists and psychologists) with the Rorschach gave the same result. The Kelly and Goldberg (1959) studies of psychologists, utilizing very extensive and varied psychological techniques, resulted in some moderately consistent personality patterns and predictors of later success for academicians and administrators, but most of the variables failed to discriminate therapists at all. The most significant conclusion from all of these studies seems to be the one drawn by Luborsky (1952) : the best predictor of success as a psychotherapist is how well the therapist is liked.

The Strong Vocational Interest Blank (SVIB) has been as effective a predictor of vocational choice and success (defined as continuation in the field) as any measure currently available to us. It was one of the few measures that gave any prediction of success in training for psychologists, and it has also proved useful with psychiatrists. Some of the scales have proved useful negatively, e.g., the less interests resemble those of a production manager, the better the prediction of success as a psychiatrist.

The supplementary Medical Specialist Preference Blank for the SVIB, intended to discriminate among pathology, internal medicine, psychiatry, and surgery, was found not to predict eventual specialty, except for psychiatrists. Campbell (1966) has recently reanalyzed the data with the same result. He also developed further specialty scales, but these too have proved disappointing. For our purposes, however, it is of particular interest to note that again the psychiatrists seemed to differ most from the others: they were more social-service-oriented and more interested in cultural esthetic activities. They were also the most feminine on the Mf

scale, differing from surgeons on this scale by one full standard deviation.

Klein, MacNair, and Lorr (1962) have studied SVIB scores of clinical psychologists, psychiatrists, and psychiatric social workers:

Compared with social workers, both psychologists and psychiatrists had higher interests in the biological science and physical science areas and more often rejected the business detail area. Social workers had higher social welfare interests than psychiatrists or psychologists. In the verbal-persuasive area, all three disciplines differed significantly from each other with social workers showing least rejection and psychiatrists most rejection of the area (pp. 177–178).

Wheelis (1956), in his discussion of the various inner circumstances that may lead to the choice of psychoanalysis as a career, sees the major determining situations as being the need for insight in a struggle for self-mastery or the need for intimacy.

Sharaf and Levinson (1964) have noted that a "quest for omnipotence" is a regularly observed theme in psychiatric residents and have explored the dynamics of this.

The Allport-Vernon Scale of Values has also proved useful in group differentiation where relatively high theoretical and esthetic values predominate. There are, of course, gross individual differences observed. Funkenstein (1965), in discussing medical student values, remarks on the fact that medical educators, as well as the public in general, deplore high economic values in the physician. He questions how premedical and medical educators meet the problem of the student with high economic values, and asks if it is possible to change the values of such materially oriented students, since they so reflect the values of the society to which they return when their education is complete. (I cite this as further pointing to the need to go beyond averages and deviations from the average, and look at the meaning to the individuals involved.)

Using techniques based on the semantic differential, Christie and Merton (1958) instituted sociological studies of the values climate of medical schools, and have shown their application to such problems as student congruence with these values. Their report does not differentiate among medical specialties, but the system is, of course, applicable to these also.

I know of no reports indicating selection of these occupations as related to socioeconomic background of the family other than relations commonly found in distinguishing those who do and do not go to college. Kelly and Goldberg (1959) noted that in comparison with other psychologists, the therapist was likely to be the eldest child in a Jewish family who had considerable friction with his father [5] and a deep attachment to his mother. As a child the therapist was likely to have experienced feel-

---

5. This was also true in general of the research psychologists I studied.

ings of inferiority and, much like academicians, a disinclination toward athletics.

Social Workers

Social workers tend to the same pattern of somewhat better verbal than quantitative aptitudes. As one would expect, they are strongly person-oriented in interests and values. Like nursing, social work is a fully accepted occupation for women, and one would not expect the aberrant life-history patterns that show up for women engineers, for example. Nevertheless, several studies (Berengarten, 1949; Roe and Siegelman, 1964; Utton, 1962) have found some early patterns of difficulties in relationships within the family. Berengarten (1949) noted, in studying twelve best- and twelve poorest-rated first-quarter students, that one of the common denominators in both groups was the experience of having had difficult relationships in their growing-up. Different basic motivations showed up in the two groups. This is a pilot study and has not been replicated, but is of considerable interest for its thoughtful analysis of motivations. In my own studies, the family backgrounds of the male social workers were more often stressful than those of the women, and their entrance into the profession much less straightforward. Nachmann's (1960) thesis compared advanced male students in social work with those in law and dentistry. She derived a number of hypotheses regarding early experiences from psychoanalytic theory, and her data confirmed the presence in the group of absent, weak, or inadequate fathers; strong, adequate, and dominant mothers; intermediate verbal skills and intellectual development; more acceptance of aggressive impulses; severe or traumatic deprivation in the first and second years; and more frequent early concern for feelings of others.

Nurses

It sometimes seems that student nurses have been as much research captives as have psychology students. Few of these studies show consistent differences in intelligence or aptitudes from students in general of the same backgrounds and colleges. Anderson and McManus (1942) reported that fathers of nursing candidates tended to be engaged in trades or manufacturing rather than in professions. Comparisons with specific groups of students may show more differentiation (e.g., Schmidt [1951] found occupational therapy (OT) students somewhat higher on a number of Wechsler-Bellevue scales), but the overlap is considerable. Schmidt found no significant differences between these same groups on the MMPI but did find some on the Rorschach; these differences have not, so far as I know, been replicated. They indicated that the OT group was more productive and better able to generalize and abstract; had a healthier respect for reality and was quicker to respond; conformed more readily to popular thinking but at the same time was less stereotyped; was more strongly self-willed but less sensitive in self-appraisal; and was more extratensive. In interest tests, nurses in general tend to come out with relatively high scores on social welfare scales and on science scales.

Cleveland (1961) reported a TAT study of student (psychiatric) and staff (some psychiatric) nurses and student and staff dietitians. He found greater differences between the student groups than between the staff groups (a warning note). The nurses scored significantly higher on passivity themes, use of distress words, sad-lonely words, and negative parental attitudes, and scored lower on achievement and positive parental attitudes. Both occupational groups gave contact with people as major reasons for choosing these professions, but the nurses stressed service to others, and the dietitians stressed influencing others for their own good. Nurses generally made career choices earlier (always wanted to be), dietitians usually not until the second year of college. Both student and staff dietitians saw their professions as offering intellectual stimulation and challenge, as did staff nurses; but student nurses thought job security more important. The gaining of self-understanding and religious motivations also tend to decline with experience in nursing. Prediction of clinical performance on the basis of tests has been generally unsatisfactory.

A study of relationships between basic motivations for nursing and the concept of the profession showed considerable correspondence within the individual, but also differences in both variables were found among individuals—i.e., the same profession is often seen in different ways by different persons and may be chosen for different reasons (Furst, Raygor, and Crofoot, 1962).

Fox, Diamond, and Jacobowsky (1961) have studied career decisions and professional expectations of nursing students for the Institute of Research and Service in Nursing Education. Their report includes data on sources of information about school selected (diploma and degree schools are handled separately throughout) but not about the profession in general. It also includes information on doubts about the wisdom of their choices, and how these are resolved. About one-half the students planned to go into general nursing, and from one-fourth to one-half (in different years) into a specialty, but these are not separately listed. With the estimate that about one third of those who enroll in nursing programs withdraw before completing their studies, the final numbers going into psychiatric nursing must be very small indeed.

Triggs (1947) compared early experiences of graduate students in nursing, mathematics, and science, finding no early differences in parental behavior but significantly greater childhood interest in gadgets and things in the math and science group.

Navran and Stauffacher (1957) have studied psychiatric nurses, using the Edwards Personal Preference Schedule. The findings suggest that the

best-rated psychiatric nurses are relatively less timid, warmer in interpersonal relationships, more stable, and more capable of leadership than
other, less highly rated nurses. Williamson, Edmondston, and Stern
(1963) found that nurses from a general hospital scored higher in he-
terosexuality and lower in abasement and endurance than the psychiatric
nurses reported by Navran and Stauffacher.

When state-hospital psychiatric nurses were compared with operating-
room nurses, they were reported by Boruchow (1965) to be less dependent and submissive to the physician, to have higher self-concepts, and
to prefer assuming authority to being directed. They also placed more
value on interpersonal relationships, and were more outspoken and
extroverted.

In a study of registered nurses in a private psychiatric hospital, Segal
(1964) has observed that, in general, as the social status of the nurses de-
creases, their emphasis on the honorific status accouterments of nursing
increases, as does their discomfort in working with patients whose extra-
hospital social status is high.

Occupational Therapists

Mention has already been made of Schmidt's (1951) studies contrasting
OT students with nursing students. A series of studies by Dunteman,
Anderson, and Barry (1966) contrasts students intending to major in
occupational therapy, physical therapy, and medical technology in a
college of health-related professions. To a considerable extent, these students are primarily oriented to physical rehabilitative work, and the possible differences from OT's in mental-hospital settings are unknown (to
me, at least). The OT's were somewhat lower than the others on quantitative tests. Factor analyses of the Strong predicted group membership
very effectively. Neither these authors nor others have been able to predict clinical performance on the basis of any tests or combinations of
them. In Utton's (1962) study, OT's at a psychiatric hospital did not
recall their relations with their parents in childhood as being particularly
stressful.

Psychiatric Aides

Kline's (1950) study of psychiatric aides reminds one of Luborsky's
(1952) findings on psychiatrists. The satisfactory aide tends to be single,
under 40, from a small town, from an intact home, and with a stable
parental marriage. He has good health and has taken the job for economic reasons or for experience. The unsatisfactory aide is likely to have
been married but to be divorced or separated, and this is likely to have
been true of his parents, who he feels are disappointed in him. His reason
for taking the job is a desire for security. A later study by Butterfield and

Warren (1962) found that MMPI scores are not related to competency of aides.

Although a majority of psychiatric aides give extrinsic reasons for taking their jobs (Simpson and Simpson, 1959), only half of them give such reasons for remaining on them. The intrinsic reasons derive chiefly from the importance of the aide in patient care; a factor they had not anticipated. With the high turnover problems in this group, it is clear that any changes that might bring increased job satisfaction are important. Although the aides considered patient care the most important aspect of their jobs, they reported that housekeeping was the most time-consuming.

IMPLICATIONS AND CONCLUSIONS

It is clear that we know much less than we need to about the personal factors involved in entrance into any of these professions, although we do have leads as to the kinds of personality make-up and emotional needs that seem most suited to them. The whole field of biographies as related to choice of these vocations is practically unworked, and if results in other fields with biographical instruments are any guide, it is here that our most useful researches may be found. I strongly urge that these be undertaken.

The material of the preceding discussion does offer some suggestions for an approach to the issues with which we are confronted—recruitment and maintenance of a more nearly adequate manpower force in the occupational groups under consideration.

Is there, first, any way to increase the pulling power of these occupations? I do not find suggestions to reconstruct these jobs into a different inclusive category of "mental health occupations" very persuasive. In fact, I think that apart from its hardly being workable, it would simply perpetuate the major difficulty facing us—the "illness model," as Albee (1967) puts it. If occupations are to be reconstructed, i.e., if necessary tasks are to be differently assigned to persons with different kinds of training, it would seem more reasonable to develop them with a different model in mind. Entrenched interests are too strong for anything like a direct and simple approach to the problem, but that is not to say that nothing can be done about it. I will revert to this issue later, but here let us go along with the present occupational structure, and see where some efforts at increasing recruitment might be helpful.

Statuses are not assigned by fiat but change slowly and in rather close relation to reality. Probably the quickest way to raise occupational status is to increase income, and to do it blatantly. But this is far from enough, and unless it were backed up by increases in other things people want, the effect would be insignificant in the long run. (I would remind you that there are many blue-collar jobs that pay more than white-collar ones, but that these fall below the latter in prestige.)

Changes in job content of such a nature that individuals in the jobs could have increased responsibility, personal involvement, and satisfaction would not affect recruitment to start with but would certainly affect turnover, and quite directly. I suspect that among psychotherapists (except for interprofessional squabbles) the work is very much what each individual wants his own work to be. This would suggest that emphasis be placed on understanding the nature of job satisfactions and dissatisfactions, particularly for those concerned with day-to-day and hour-to-hour patient care, i.e., the nurses and the aides. A great deal could be done in many institutions to free both of these groups from clerical or housekeeping duties, which give little satisfaction to the kind of person who is really interested in helping people.

These suggestions essentially refer to the pulling power of these occupations. What about the matter of the individuals choosing the jobs? It seems clear that all of these jobs should primarily require that the holder be concerned with other persons in a helping way. I think it is important that this interest be on a nondefensive rather than defensive basis, but, as things are, I will not quibble about that. We do know that these attitudes are generally more feminine than masculine in our traditional culture, and they link with appropriate values and interests. I do not at the moment see any very likely way of increasing the numbers of such persons: it is my opinion that this basic person or non-person orientation is well established by kindergarten years, although I do not think that it is necessarily irreversible. Accepting this, the only appropriate tactics are to enhance and reward such attitudes throughout the life span. For girls, the culture does approve and, in that sense at least, reward nurturant attitudes, although other attitudes, previously unacceptable for women, are now accepted and to that extent compete with nurturance as a primary feminine value. For boys, there have been few real rewards for nurturant behavior—quite the contrary, in fact—although here some relaxation seems to have occurred. For example, many more young fathers are directly concerned with child care than they used to be. More such rewards could be instituted, chiefly, I think, by introducing caring experiences at an early age in homes and schools. Some moves in this direction are already in hand, and could easily be increased. For example, summer work (whether on a paid or volunteer basis) could be offered for both boys and girls in hospitals and clinics. With duties and supervision planned to emphasize interpersonal interactions, I think this could be helpful, although it would be some years before any effects were seen. I do want to emphasize the planning required. Just carting flowers around to various rooms is not the point; what is needed is more individual attention to individual patients. Such programs need judicious publicity and public rewards, e.g., for the most helping boy and girl, etc.

Since, as has been repeatedly stressed, these occupations call for many "feminine" attitudes, more attention should be paid to recruiting women into those fields in which they are in the minority—both as therapists and as psychiatric aides. In addition, realignment of hours of work and some other special arrangements should be seriously considered in order to attract women with home responsibilities who could work on a part-time basis. The chief hindrance to such arrangements is simply managerial reluctance; where they have been set up by people who really wanted them to work, they have proved satisfactory in a number of different situations.

There is a steadily increasing pool of manpower to which no real attention seems to have been given in this connection. It is well known that attitudes do change with age, and among other changes, men and women do become more alike as they get older. One of the specific changes is that most men become more nurturant and more interested in people and in interaction with them. When one adds to this the fact that men are living longer and retiring earlier, the possibilities are suddenly striking. I think it entirely possible that many retired men could make a very great contribution in these ways, even with minimal training. Again, some imaginative realignment of duties and genuinely cooperative management are required. Furthermore, the presence in such positions of successful business and professional men should have a considerable effect on youngsters who might otherwise be reluctant to risk their manliness. I have not even mentioned the satisfactions for the men themselves; these seem self-evident.

Explicit in some of the above suggestions, and implicit in all of the others, is a need for more public knowledge of job and career possibilities. This should begin in the early years and continue throughout the educational process. It should also be widely developed for recruitment of nonprofessionals for the new roles suggested above.

Finally, let me revert to the point mentioned earlier: the need for reconstruction of this whole effort in other terms. I agree completely with Albee (1967) that maintenance of the illness model is hampering all of our efforts. It may, however, have one effect that could be considered useful from a manpower point of view: many people might be reluctant to go to a mental health clinic because of the imputation of insanity.

They might, however, be willing to go to something called a "Community Resources Center," and might even be willing to go early enough to forestall entrenching of their difficulties. My idea of such a center is pretty well explained by the name. It should include a great deal more than the kinds of services now subsumed under the mental health concept—namely, educational, vocational and recreational advice, welfare services, etc. In short, it should be the place any citizen would consider first when he wasn't sure what to do or where to turn for help in a situation. In many situations it obviously would function simply as a referral agency. And I might add that many of its staff would require relatively little training, much less than a doctoral education, and might well permit creation of new occupations and careers not bound by the stereotypes of the past.

REFERENCES

ABEL, T. M., S. OPPENHEIM, and C. J. SAGER. 1956. Screening applicants for training in psychoanalytically oriented psychotherapy. *American Journal of Psychotherapy*, 10:24–37.

ALBEE, G. W. 1967. The relation of conceptual models to manpower needs. In E. L. Cowen, E. A. Gardner, and M. Zax (Eds.), *Emergent approaches to mental health problems*. New York: Appleton-Century-Crofts.

ANDERSON, M. H., and R. L. McMANUS. 1942. Interests of nursing candidates: The pattern of interests and activities of 800 prenursing students. *American Journal of Nursing*, 42:555–563.

BARKER, D. G. 1964. Concepts of disabilities. *Personnel and Guidance Journal*, 43:371–374.

BERGENGARTEN, S. 1949. A pilot study to establish criteria for selection of students in social work. (Mimeo.)

BORUCHOW, J. K. 1965. Characteristics of nurses in short- and long-term treatment settings. *Journal of Social Psychology*, 67:61–66.

BUTTERFIELD, E. C., and S. A. WARREN. 1962. The use of the MMPI in the selection of hospital aides. *Journal of Applied Psychology*, 46:34–40.

CAMPBELL, D. P. 1966. Re-analysis of Strong's interest data from medical specialists. Final report for U.S. Office of Education, December. (Mimeo.)

CHRISTIE, R., and R. K. MERTON. 1958. Procedures for the sociological study of the values climate of medical schools. In H. H. Gee and R. J. Glaser (Eds.), *The ecology of the medical student*. Report of the Fifth Teaching Institute of the Association of American Medical Colleges, Atlantic City, October, 1957. Evanston, Ill.: Association of American Medical Colleges.

CLEVELAND, S. 1961. Personality patterns associated with the professions of dietician and nurse. *Journal of Health and Human Behavior*, 2:113–124.

COOLEY, W. W. 1963. *Career development of scientists: an overlapping longitudinal study*. Graduate School of Education, Harvard University. Cooperative Research Project No. 436, Office of Education, HEW.

DUNTEMAN, G. H., H. E. ANDERSON, and J. R. BARRY. 1966. *Characteristics of students in the health related professions*. University of Florida Rehabilitation Research Monograph Series, No. 2.

ERON, L. D. 1954. Use of the Rorschach method in medical student selection. *Journal of Medical Education*, 20:35–39.

FOX, D. J., L. K. DIAMOND, and N. JOCOBOWSKY. 1961. *Career decisions and professional expectations of nursing students*. New York: Teachers College, Columbia University.

FUNKENSTEIN, D. H. 1965. Current problems in the verbal and quantitative ability subtests of the Medical College Admission Test. *Journal of Medical Education*, 40:1031–48.

FURST, E. J., A. W. RAYGOR, and A. P. CROFOOT. 1962. Basic motivation and concept of nursing as chosen profession. *Journal of Psychology*, 54:85–100.

KELLY, E. L., and L. R. GOLDBERG. 1959. Correlates of later performance and specialization in psychology. *Psychological Monographs*, 73, No. 12.

KLEIN, F. L., D. M. McNAIR, and M. LORR. 1962. SVIB scores of clinical psychologists, psychiatrists, and social workers. *Journal of Counseling Psychology*, 9:176–179.

KLINE, N. S. 1950. Characteristics and screening of unsatisfactory psychiatric attendants and attendant-applicants. *American Journal of Psychiatry*, 106: 573–586.

LUBORSKY, L. 1952. The personality of the psychotherapist. *Menninger Quarterly*, 6:1–6.

———, and R. R. HOLT. 1957. The selection of candidates for psychoanalytic training. *Journal of Clinical and Experimental Psychopathology*, 18:166–176.

NACHMANN, B. 1960. Childhood experience and vocational choice in law, dentistry, and social work. *Journal of Counseling Psychology*, 7:243–250.

NAVRAN, L., and J. C. STAUFFACHER. 1957. The personality structure of psychiatric nurses. *Nursing Research*, 5:109–114.

O'DOWD, D. D., and D. C. BEARDSLEE. 1960. *College student images of a selected group of professions and occupations.* Cooperative Research Project No. 562. Middletown, Conn.: Wesleyan University.

ROE, A. 1956. *The psychology of occupations.* New York: Wiley.

———. 1966. Women and work. Review of E. Ginzberg, *Life styles of educated women. Science*, 153:965–966.

———, and M. SIEGELMAN. 1964. *The origin of interests.* Washington, D.C.: American Personnel and Guidance Association.

SCHMIDT, H. O. 1951. Comparison of women students in occupational therapy and in nursing. *Journal of Psychology*, 31:161–174.

SCHOFIELD, W. 1953. A study of medical students with the MMPI: I. Scale norms and profile patterns. *Journal of Psychology*, 36:59–65.

SEGAL, B. E. 1964. Nurses and patients: a case study in stratification. *Journal of Health and Human Behavior*, 5:54–60.

SHARAF, M. R., and D. J. LEVINSON. 1964. The quest for omnipotence in professional training. *Psychiatry*, 27:135–149.

SIMPSON, R. L., and I. H. SIMPSON. 1959. The psychiatric attendant: development of an occupational self-image in a low-status occupation. *American Sociological Review*, 24:389–392.

TRIGGS, F. O. 1947. The measured interests of nurses. *Journal of Educational Research*, 41:25–34.

U.S. Labor Department, Bureau of Employment Security. 1965. *Dictionary of Occupational Titles.* 2 vols. (3d ed.) Washington, D.C.: U.S. Government Printing Office.

U.S. Labor Department, Bureau of Labor Statistics. 1966. *Occupational Outlook Handbook.* (1966–67 ed.) Washington, D.C.: U.S. Government Printing Office.

UTTON, A. C. 1962. Recalled parent-child relations as determinants of vocational choice. *Journal of Counseling Psychology*, 9:49–53.

WHEELIS, A. 1956. The vocational hazards of psychoanalysis. *International Journal of Psychoanalysis*, 37:171–184.

WILLIAMSON, H. M., W. E. EDMONSTON, JR., and J. A. STERN. 1963. Use of the EPPS for identifying personal role attributes desirable in nursing. *Journal of Health and Human Behavior*, 4:266–275.

CHAPTER 8

The New Mental Health Workers

FRANKLYN N. ARNHOFF,
JOAN W. JENKINS, AND
JOSEPH C. SPEISMAN

ONE OF THE MOST significant factors affecting the mental health field at this time is the recent upsurge in interest in new types of mental health workers. Typically, these people are seen as functioning in a technical, assisting relationship to traditional mental health professionals, although in some instances independent functions are portrayed. While the possibility of utilizing such personnel has been discussed periodically since World War II, it is only within the past five years or so that any meaningful effort has been made to define the tasks these people might perform, to develop training programs, and to create employment opportunities for them.

The report of the Joint Commission on Mental Illness and Health (1961) did not specifically recommend creation of new types of mental health workers, but the general suggestions that were made within the context of gloomy predictions of a continued shortage of training professionals were relevant (Albee, 1959). It was recommended that a major recruitment drive be undertaken through training programs for all categories of mental health personnel, including on-the-job training in the subprofessions and upgrading for partially trained persons. It was further recommended that in order to provide services to mentally troubled individuals in the absence of fully trained professionals, persons with some psychological orientation should provide preventative counseling in the community. To this end the suggestion was made that mental health counselors be obtained by affording brief training to clergymen, family physicians, teachers, probation officers, public health nurses, sheriffs, judges, public welfare workers, scoutmasters, county farm agents, and others. Such individuals would be supervised in the community by fully trained professionals. In addition, the commission suggested that pediatricians and special kinds of teachers were key groups who should be provided with adequate psychiatric information. Since these recommendations were made, almost all of the groups named above have been brought into the mental health arena, and under the leadership of the various programs of the National Institute of Mental Health (NIMH), support has been made available for their training (NIMH, 1967). While the involvement of these types of people in mental health activities is relatively new in and of itself, the current trend extends even beyond this and deals most specifically with the development of new types of workers: subprofessionals and nonprofessionals to deal with the mentally disturbed in all facets of societal functions and institutions. This trend in increasing the involvement of ever larger numbers of persons is a continuing reflection of a perceived manpower shortage, which in turn reflects the expanding concepts of need in the mental health area.

Increased need in the mental health field is evidenced by a few selected statistics. While the mental hospital census has been declining slightly, although steadily, since 1955, admissions have been rising at a rate of 7.4 per cent a year (Kramer, 1966). Thus, there is an increasing number of people in and out of mental hospitals who can be expected to need rehabilitation and support in the community. The number of people seen in outpatient clinics has risen 62 per cent in the years 1960–63, and long waiting lists are usual (Kramer, 1966). Since the population continues to grow, there are more mentally retarded, and the absolute number will progressively increase as a function of the population growth per se. The rise in people seeking treatment is especially rapid in the younger age groups for both residential and outpatient care. Since this is the segment of the population that is growing fastest, the combined increase in both number and rate makes this a critical area.

Statistics such as these are the foundations upon which conceptions of increasing need are based, since it is apparent, given our present social philosophy, that these problems demand attention. What is unclear is the manner in which they are to be handled, and the mechanisms, in terms of manpower, legislation, and education, that may be best mobilized and utilized in finding solutions. The trend toward new types of personnel is just one alternative. Evaluation of the mental health problems, the apparent manpower shortages, and the proposed solutions involve issues on a conceptual level that transcend the mental health fields alone.

The development of new occupations in the mental health field, primarily at the subprofessional level, is corollary to, if not an outgrowth of, a similar pattern in the broader areas of human services and health services in general. In these broader areas, the last few years have seen considerable development of increased opportunities for new types of subprofessional and technical personnel, as well as an emphasis upon greater utilization of the nonprofessional, primarily from the lower socioeconomic groups.

This use of ancillary personnel has had two main causes, based upon quite different considerations, but both with direct implications for manpower utilization, manpower shortages, and expansion of the labor pool; the first is the advance in health technology, and the second, the social welfare–educational legislation of the past few years. In the field of health services, advances in health technology have already resulted in marked changes in practice and patient care and are viewed as having the potential for even greater ultimate impact on the nature and number of jobs in the health field. It is expected that these technological advances will continue to increase and, with increasing adoption, will result in greater productivity in the health service field (Sturm, 1967). The anticipated continued employment growth in this area is expressed in the projections of the Bureau of Labor Statistics. Exclusive of physicians and dentists, there were 2.7 million full-time equivalent jobs in the health service industry in 1965, which will rise to 3.1 million in 1970 and 3.6 million in 1975. During the past few years, especially since the enactment of the Manpower Development and Training Act (1962), the Vocational Education Act (1963), the Health Professions Education Act (1963), and the Nurse Training Act (1964), provisions for training professional and nonprofessional workers for health-related jobs have steadily expanded (Sturm, 1967).

Federal legislative acts directed primarily toward the elimination of poverty and the improvement of elementary and secondary education also have a direct impact on mental health manpower problems. It has been estimated that there are probably close to 75,000 nonprofessionals now in jobs created by antipoverty legislation, an estimated 30,000 teachers' aides to be employed through Title I of the Elementary and Secondary Education Act, and many thousands more to be utilized as home-health aides through Medicare (Goldberg, 1967). The National Commission on Technology, Automation, and Economic Progress (1966) has estimated that continued expanded public service employment in six categories where social needs are now inadequately met, if indeed they are met at all, would create 5.3 million new jobs for people with relatively low skills.

With the development of broad societal trends to employ semiskilled or unskilled personnel in the health areas, there has been a concomitant, mounting realization in mental health that it will never be possible to train the necessary numbers of psychiatrists, psychologists, social workers, and psychiatric nurses. Despite the rates of growth of these professions, they have only marginally managed to keep ahead of the growth in population. While there is some possibility of educating even greater numbers of such persons, no reasonable estimates have ever assumed that it is possible to train enough to meet conceptions of need, present or projected. A further factor of increasing influence in pressing for alternative methods of solution has been growing acceptance of the various studies and writings regarding the limited effectiveness of traditional approaches to treatment and their applicability, even if they were universally available, to all population segments (Brill and Storrow, 1960; Eysenck, 1966; Miller and Mishler, 1959).

Certainly it has not been demonstrated that all forms of disturbed behavior and mental illness are best treated by, nor do they respond best to, traditional methods of psychotherapy, most commonly illustrated by the one-to-one verbal approach, which usually is quite costly of time. The effectiveness of these methods for the total range of people and social classes is also in question; it has been shown that many patients actually reject such a treatment approach. Members of the lower socioeconomic groups in particular often demand direction and medication and will leave treatment if these are not forthcoming (Imber, Nash, and Stone, 1955; Overall and Aronson, 1963). As to the large number of borderline mentally ill—that is, those who return to the community after hospitalization and may well require future hospitalization—they most often profit from vocational and social rehabilitation rather than traditional psychotherapy (Levine, 1964; McMahon, 1964; Massimo and Shore, 1963). Findings such as these, coupled with an obvious and increasing inability of the traditional professional groups to deal with the magnitude of the tasks presented by society, have led to greater consideration and effort to seek new, different, and less costly types of personnel who can be drawn from a different segment of the total potential labor pool than is usual for mental health occupations.

The nature and extent of available resources and manpower currently involved in mental health cannot, however, be assessed by focusing only on mental health professionals and hospital-clinic statistics, since these give, at best, a partial picture of current activity and involvement.

There is little doubt that most of the therapy, counseling, guidance, and solace in what is broadly termed the mental health field is done by many people whose roles are not usually thought of as being primarily in this area. Despite the tremendous improvement in the public's acceptance of mental disturbance, only a small part of the total population seeks out mental health professionals for help with their personal problems of living. The most definitive study in this area was reported in the book *Americans View Their Mental Health*, by Gurin, Veroff, and Feld (1960). They reported that of those people in their sample who said that they had once sought professional help for a personal problem, 42 per cent had gone to their clergyman and 29 per cent to their physician. Others had gone to lawyers, teachers, judges, and policemen, and only a minority saw a psychiatrist, psychologist, or social worker. Many people will not complete a referral to a psychiatrist or psychologist because they do not recognize these professions as needed for other than severe emotional disturbance (Arnhoff, 1966; Gurin, Veroff, and Feld, 1960). In another recent study, Thumin and Zebelman (1967) reported that more than 25 per cent of their sample would seek out their physician or minister for marital problems, and 38 per cent would seek help for excessive drinking from their minister or Alcoholics Anonymous. Since there are more than 300,000 physicians and about 400,000 recognized clergymen in this country, it is obvious that most mental health practice is by people not in the traditional mental health disciplines (Ryan, 1967). Because of the nature of their activities, such professionals come into contact with troubled people seeking counseling and advice; problems that must be recognized and dealt with in some way. Furthermore, there is little or no stigma attached to seeing clergymen or physicians, whereas there may be if one seeks help from a mental health professional. If we combine the numbers of persons involved in problems of human behavior and adjustment in their daily professional functions with the numbers of primary mental health professionals described and enumerated in Chapter 1, it is obvious that a huge segment of society is already involved in attempting to provide mental health services to the rest of the population (Arnhoff, 1967). Still, the total number is not seen as adequate, and many persons who want or need help are unable to obtain it.

The broad range of people described above are active in mental health affairs by virtue of their primary professional functions, which also involve human problems and conflicts. The new types of mental health workers, on the other hand, are persons whose jobs call for full-time primary involvement with the mentally disturbed or retarded. Since their employment is not a matter of contemplation, but rather of actuality, it might be well to describe some of the ongoing training and duties of these people before any further discussion or assessment.

In mental institutions in the past, there was often a wide and unfilled gap between the psychiatrist in charge of the hospital or ward, with hundreds of patients in his care, and the aide, usually uneducated and untrained, who actually dealt with the patient. With the twin realizations that many patients can be rehabilitated and discharged, and that a prolonged stay in an institution has in itself a deleterious effect, efforts have been made to recruit and train personnel who will care for the patients in an enlightened and informed manner. The most widespread of these is the Hospital Staff Development Program of the NIMH for psychiatric aides in mental institutions, a program specifically aimed at improving and upgrading hospital aides and attendants.

Other efforts have been smaller, but they are interesting for their innovations. The Devereux Foundation has a multidisciplinary training program of twelve months' duration for prospective houseparents, the graduates receiving a certificate in child care. An attempt is being made to evaluate selection procedures, such as the desirability of a high school diploma, and to find tests which may be predictive of a "good" houseparent as well as to assess and specify the criteria of success.

Another program to train personnel to care for retarded or disturbed children is being developed at the Western Psychiatric Institute. One project gives two years of training, including a year of internship, to high school graduates and leads to a certificate in child care. The other project admits college graduates who have majored in psychology, sociology, social work, education, nursing, or child areas to an interdisciplinary program of at least five trimesters leading to a master of science in child development.

Knox College has a B.A. program in human development to prepare its graduates to be "child-care specialists." They are qualified to work under minimal supervision with outpatient or resident children in a position described as higher than aides and lower than specialists. Their knowledge of the fields of psychology and education enables them to carry out the recommendations of the staff in a skilled and understanding manner.

Although these programs are training people with different backgrounds, from less than a high school education to the bachelor's degree, and consequently preparing them for different levels of responsibility, all are aimed at filling the gap between unskilled aide and highly trained professional in providing better care for the institutionalized and disturbed child.

Another type of training is being provided by Philadelphia State Hospital. College graduates are being trained as "social interaction therapists" to work with chronic schizophrenics, with the aim of enabling the patients to modify their maladaptive behavior patterns and respond in a more socially acceptable fashion. Possible places of employment, besides mental institutions, are day-care programs, halfway houses, sheltered workshops, and community clinics.

Somewhat similar is the program at the Rockford Zone Center in Illinois. College graduates are given twelve months' training leading to a master's degree and the title "mental health reentry expediter." They are expected to function as part of a team helping ex-patients adjust to the community and preventing their rehospitalization. Their work is primarily with a group known for its high hospitalization risk and low social competence.

Albert Einstein College of Medicine of Yeshiva University, in New York, is experimenting with utilizing the skills of mature housewives whose children are old enough not to require their constant care. These women are given part-time training for nine months in the rehabilitation of the socially disabled. Receiving the title "mental health rehabilitation counselor," they become a quasi-relative to a discharged mental patient, helping him in the areas of housing, social life, work, and daily living, with the aim of giving support, not insight.

This use of the middle-aged (or "mature") woman as a source of relatively sophisticated labor, either as a semiprofessional or a volunteer, is receiving increasing recognition. Probably the best-known such project is that of Margaret Rioch in training housewives (all college graduates) to be mental health counselors, primarily in outpatient or college clinics. In an allied program, similar women were prepared for jobs as child development counselors to work in well-baby clinics, nursery schools, etc.

While the above jobs are considered to be both salaried and professional, volunteer organizations welcome the smaller amounts of unpaid time that can be given to them. Inservice training and supervision have enabled women to assume the full range of duties at a suicide-prevention center in Los Angeles. Other communities want volunteers to work with deprived or maladjusted children and adolescents as tutors, companions, counselors, vocational instructors, recreational aides, chauffeurs, etc. Project Promise, in Alexandria, Virginia, is looking for "men and women who can relate warmly to other human beings" to work with unwed mothers, culturally and emotionally deprived children, and former patients of the state mental hospital. The examples presented above, some limited to inpatient activities and others appropriate either for hospital, clinic, or community mental health center, have focused on specific jobs and rather specific activities.

Another growing area of development is not specific to any one type of job but rather is an attempt to develop an educational source as a pool to increase the manpower supply for mental health agencies and activities by involving the community and junior colleges. People in these programs are envisioned as receiving two years of college training as preparation for employment in the mental health services area.

This method of increasing the manpower supply in mental health agencies has received very thoughtful consideration from many groups, including the Southern Regional Education Board (1966). They note that community colleges are a rapidly developing part of the American education scene and, because of their ties to their local area, give particular attention to serving the needs of the community. They envisage the creation of a "middle-level mental health worker" who could perform a wide variety of tasks in hospitals, clinics, schools, and other public agencies, and would be well trained in the principles of mental health and the specifics of service work. Purdue University, for example, has started a two-year program leading to an associate of arts degree as a generalized mental health worker equipped to work with patients both in and out of institutions.

The biggest innovation in mental health services for noninstitutionalized people, in terms of both type and number, is the attempt to develop a person to work with those members of society of marginal social competence, whether they are traditionally classified as "mentally ill" or not. This is a result of several recent trends, one of which is the attempt to get patients out of the hospital, resulting in increased numbers of psychotics in remission trying to make their way in the community, often without the resources or competence to do so. Another important force is the war on poverty, which has become tied in with the whole mental health movement. Thus, health, education, welfare, civil rights, and social protest have become intermingled, and a person working in any of these areas is seen as contributing to all the others. Finally, there are the growing problems of alcoholism and drug addiction, which are now seen as "illnesses," with recent court decisions stating that these people must receive mental health treatment.

The Community Mental Health Centers' construction and staffing acts are an attempt to alleviate these problems, as are the Antipoverty and Community Action Programs. Trained personnel have not, however, been easy to find, both because of the well-known preference of the middle-class professional to work with middle-class patients, and because of the often unrewarding and interminable task of dealing with people of low motivation, limited assets, and large liabilities. This type of person can be epitomized in the skid-row alcoholic or the schizophrenic of low intelligence who has been repeatedly hospitalized, and for whom continued, periodic rehospitalization can be anticipated. It is here that the emerging use of the nonprofessional is most noticeable.

A project at Albert Einstein, aimed specifically at target groups such as these, is training "community mental health aides" in conjunction with Lincoln Hospital. These aides are recruited from the deprived, low-income, or unemployed residents of the community and given training in various social agencies. They are then placed in a neighborhood center, where their job is to give guidance to the poor in almost all areas: filling out forms, acting as a tutor or club leader, and serving as liaison with the school, hospital, and social-welfare agency. This is the so-called indigenous nonprofessional, and it is estimated by some that at least a million of these should be employed in public service (Pearl and Reissman, 1965). While their exact function is hotly debated, being variously seen as a way of reducing unemployment, bridging the communication gap between the professional and the client, making the large public-welfare agency more responsive to the needs of low-income minority-group clientele, or creating a viable place in society for the poor and a mechanism for social change, their use is certainly on the increase.

The brief descriptions given are a mere sample of the programs and methods devised to train new types of workers in mental health. All are in response to tremendous mounting social pressure for something to be done, with the understanding that the traditional professions cannot by themselves handle the task. Any attempts at understanding, much less assessment, of the projects described involve at least brief mention of an extremely wide and complex range of phenomena.

First, as to the origins of this movement: In a previous section we mentioned the corollary developments in the total health and human services field, indicating that broad, sweeping social legislation was one force, and that technological developments were the second. Technology itself has spawned many new jobs in all areas, medical technology being just one. Such, however, is not the case in mental health, where technology is still quite primitive. This is true partly because the complexity of the problems involved has defied genuine analysis, and even the most sophisticated approaches have tended to see mental health in monolithic terms. Technological practices of only a decade ago, such as electroconvulsive shock, insulin shock, and lobotomy, are seen today as being of very limited utility and applicability. Except for the introduction of some new drugs for behavioral control, practice is essentially as it was, technologically, when the fields began. Psychological techniques of behavior modification via operant conditioning or other developments promise change, but as yet such procedures are in their infancy. Thus, the drive for more manpower and the new types of workers has as its base not new technology and knowledge but rather increased social awareness and demand for social action.

The demand for social action is a major key to understanding the recent developments in the mental health movement. We can place the new workers in the proper perspective of one possible alternative, chosen on the basis of existing conceptions and models. Without prejudging in any manner the effectiveness or benefit that may accrue from this choice, it is important to realize that other choices are possible and may have more extensive payoff.

As the total fabric of society has changed and evolved as a function of tremendous technological development, unprecedented population expansion, and increased social and physical mobility, so have changes occurred in the social community and the nuclear family of the past. Older patterns of responsibility for the caretaking of the elderly, the sick, the demented, and even the young and healthy increasingly appear within the purview of the total society, in contrast to remaining as the limited concern of the immediate family or community. From the major social legislation of the 1930's, such as the Social Security laws, through to the New Frontier and the Great Society conceptions, with their enabling legislation, the general aims of our culture have been broadened to seek economic security for all, as well as an active establishment of the rights of all members of the society to full participation in the opportunities that are afforded.

This is especially true of those groups considered to be deprived or underprivileged in one way or another. Minority groups now have legal claim upon educational systems, economic benefits, housing, etc., through a variety of laws, such as the Education Act, Poverty, Civil Rights, Medicare, etc. The broad social, economic, and political forces occurring in our society that are represented by this legislation have also directly affected the mental health area and, in fact, have led to legislation specific to this area. The community mental health construction and staffing acts, the drug-abuse laws, and, on a more local level, a variety of acts concerning the status of alcoholics and the judicial concern with the legal status of insanity, are all reflective of the parallel between what is happening in the mental health field and what is happening in society in general. In fact, one must see the interaction of these forces as more than mere parallels, since the element of greatest concern to the Great Society programs is in general identical with the newer concerns that are now included under the rubric "mental health."

The expanding parameters included under the umbrella of mental health offer the next avenue for understanding what has transpired. While "mental health" was first used (and still is) interchangeably with "mental illness," it has come to include an ever increasing range of social-behavioral phenomena that previously were excluded, or at most only tangentially related. Thus, "sick," "pathological," and related illness terms are used, as well as newer conceptions, such as "culturally deprived," etc. The result is the paradox of mental health manpower: increased recruitment, training programs, and manpower production are unable to keep pace with perceived need.

If we go back a moment to mental illness as traditionally defined, the need dimension becomes clearer. It has frequently been noted that on the basis of available evidence, there has been essentially no increase in the rate of serious mental disturbance (psychosis) during early and middle life over the last century (Goldhammer and Marshall, 1953). The increase in services required for the modern urban community "probably cannot be accounted for, except to a relatively modest degree, by an accelerated incidence of individual and social breakdown. The absence or rejection of primary group support systems and changing expectations of adequate care account for much of the increased demand" (Mencher, 1964, p. 3).

In this regard, it has been observed that "the need for supplements to the contemporary system of social relationships is not synonymous with individual or social breakdown. The linking of aid and pathology is consistent with an outmoded concept of social institutions and social welfare based on relatively isolated and independent social units whose failure was marked by recourse to 'residual' social welfare functions" (Mencher, 1964, p. 4).

Mencher (1964) has described the expansion of social welfare on the impersonal side (legislation, etc.) and the resultant increase in demand for personal services. Middle-class values emphasize personal services, and it is the middle class that tends to monopolize health services (Abel-Smith and Titmus, 1956; Hollingshead and Redlich, 1958; Ryan, 1967). These values, however, provide the basis and the model for projecting the requirements for all of society. Following this model, manpower needs "stretch ahead without limit if contemporary patterns of service are the accepted model" (Mencher, 1964, p. 7). These needs after all are social values, which may incorporate professional judgment as to what is socially desirable and the goals to strive for. Since they represent an ideal, these projections of manpower needs must be confronted with realistic hopes of attainment along a temporal dimension. The societal values inculcated being the existing middle-class ones of individual professional service, even the development of subclasses of personnel will probably have only limited impact. A further complication is the rigidifying of class lines and official sanctioning of furnishing one type and quality of service to the poor and another to the well-to-do.

There is no question that society has changed drastically and that there are many problems that urgently need to be addressed. Little, however, is accomplished by including these societal problems within a dimension of traditional pathology, and much may actually be inhibited by precluding the exploration and utilization of other models, which may have completely different manpower attributes in terms of types, numbers, and educational and training requirements.

Even within the broader context of health, there are considerations that are often overlooked. As Dubos (1959) has observed, any change in society, if it is significant, will result in changes, one way or another, in the health of the population. In this sense, then, the evolution of a society in major transition should be expected to provide spin-off into many areas. The history of medicine provides excellent examples, since the major advances originally made in the control and reduction of communicable disease were the result, not of health advances or changes per se, but of changes in conceptions of cleanliness and sanitation concomitant with major social upheavals.

With these many and varied considerations forming the general tableau upon which manpower issues are formed, we can turn again to the new occupations. Here issues can be stated that have direct relevance to the potential trainees as people, as well as to their roles.

For the most part, the jobs of these new workers are ill-defined and their effectiveness completely untested. Some seem a combination of social worker and clerk, and others compete for status and acceptance with highly trained professionals. For some not even a high school education is a prerequisite, while a few require graduate training. All of them present problems in both conception and application, and the solution to these problems will determine the viability of each new type.

The first, simplest, and greatest utilization of existing manpower, by giving mental health skills and knowledge to existing disciplines and professions, presents perhaps the most clear-cut problems. There is a central issue common to all efforts in the mental health field, and that is the tenuousness of the state of our knowledge. Do we know what is the best way to treat the alcoholic, drug addict, delinquent, sociopath, hysteric, or dependent personality? Can such knowledge as we have be meaningfully and effectively conveyed in a short period so that the trainee will realize both his skills and his limitations? Perhaps the only answer to this is that we must cope as best we can, and that even minimal education is a help to the people who must deal with disturbed individuals; but the issues of what they are to be taught and toward what end are major ones.

The second question is whether we may reasonably expect most physicians, teachers, lawyers, policemen, etc., to become even more actively involved in mental health. Clergymen are perhaps exempt here, as their parishioners' problems are a primary focus of their jobs; but, even here, strictly religious interest and duties occupy much of their time. The case is similar with physicians. The general practitioner must see a large number of people and has little time for counseling. In addition, he often feels more sympathetic to, and would rather treat, physical than mental ills. Teachers must emphasize imparting knowledge to their students, and may consider the emotionally disturbed child a disrupting influence rather than a challenge. Lawyers and policemen may well feel that their duty to the law conflicts with concern for the motivations or problems of the law-breaker. In short, the imparting of new knowledge and skills to these people, while undoubtedly helpful, may not enlarge the manpower pool quite as much as initially anticipated.

The development of shorter training programs to provide aides and assistants to the existing disciplines often arouses resentment in the existing professions, particularly, where it may lead to confusion about status and duties in the mind of the public or employer. The person with less formal education may, with years of experience, feel himself fully capable, but many jobs are closed to him. And the professional with an advanced degree is worried either that the possible mistakes of someone with lesser training may reflect on him or that his longer and more expensive education will not insure him greater rewards. Problems of accreditation, career advancement, responsibility, and job duties appropriate to each level also arise. These, however, are to some extent difficulties within a profession and probably must be worked out by that group.

Similar considerations arise when the new type of worker competes with an existing discipline. Rioch's "mental health counselors," although they are all working, had some problem of acceptance by their agencies, and the paths to promotion and salary increases are far from clear. A "mental health reentry expediter" may look very much like a social worker, but he has no strong organization to back him in his struggle for advancement. The problem of rewriting job classifications and finding suitable employment for these new types is a large one, and if the rewards are not commensurate with their training and abilities, they will leave the field—often to enter graduate school in a more recognized specialty. In short, this new type is dangerous if he competes with the professional, and disillusioned and dissatisfied if he doesn't. As yet, his expectations may be quite unclear, and as a result many of these training programs have vacancies.

The issues of type of training, role, duties, and possibilities for advancement are particularly controversial in the case of the "indigenous nonprofessional." Some people feel that these workers have a special sensitivity and compassion by nature of their poverty-stricken background and that this makes them more able to communicate with their clients and more effective on the job; therefore, they should be able to perform most tasks and, with experience, become supervisors and trainers themselves. Others contend that they are unskilled and bewildered in the face of the unexpected and should function primarily as aides, with relatively simple and concrete duties and always under supervision.

To answer these questions, we would need an evaluation of the effectiveness of various people and disciplines in the mental health field—a notoriously difficult proposition. There is no agreement on criteria of success, and no group presently employed has ever been evaluated in such a way.

Often there seems little choice of who is to be trained, particularly, in as low-paid an area as mental health service has traditionally been. One participant in a recent conference put it this way: "The lower half of a (high school) class is what we need to consider. We need to seek out the married woman, the domestic worker, the unskilled, and the dropouts. When the task is carefully spelled out we don't always need junior college people or the upper intelligence level. We need to look for human beings with a certain sensitivity and the ability to work with people" (South. Reg. Ed. Bd., 1966, p. 7) .

For certain types of jobs this appraisal is probably accurate. The Devereux Foundation, in its search for houseparents, gives preference to high school graduates but is careful to look for an appropriate level of vocational expectation and aspiration. The Western Psychiatric Institute feared that the first group in its certificate program, who were fairly bright recent high school graduates, might have been given aspirations that were too high. It selected its second group from older and often unemployed people in the hope that they would prove more stable in their low-paid jobs.

These examples, however, were mostly taken from people trained to work in custodial institutions, often with children and usually with the retarded. The duties were fairly routine and the patients and situations encountered unlikely to be intellectually demanding. Helping the disturbed adult, who has the whole community to stimulate or frustrate him and a great range of potential reactions, may demand more than the talents of the unskilled and the dropout.

We have not attempted a systematic analysis of the overlap in function for these new groups with existing professions or occupations such as occupational therapists, remedial teachers, hospital aides, etc. It can be assumed that the greater the overlap with existing groups, the greater the difficulty in gaining acceptance and the more the problems in establishing career patterns. Since there is already tremendous overlap in the therapeutic functions of the existing mental health disciplines, this is not a mere academic issue. Although there is absolutely no research to show differential effects on patients as a function of treatment by any one group in contrast to another, the polemic rages and the pecking order is maintained, despite considerable differences in time and cost in training these different groups.

In our zeal to provide services for those who need help, a rather unsystematic proliferation of manpower approaches has suddenly emerged, but certainly not enough attention has been paid to the people we are training. If they are taught irrelevant or obsolescent skills, what is their future employment picture? Where can they see themselves ten years after training?

Questioning the new trends and roles is not necessarily an argument for maintenance of the status quo and current professional perquisites. There is a most definite need for a reevaluation of the present professional roles and functions. There is certainly the possibility to consider, however, that if the new careers are not properly designed, if they are not really careers, service may not improve and employment may be a temporary thing (Goldberg, 1967).

In many respects, fertile ground for development of such ineffectiveness and disillusionment already exists as a result of the rather haphazard manner in which these training programs have multiplied and the often imprecise thinking and terminology used. "Mental health worker" is a generic term obviously encompassing a multitude of divergent types of persons performing many different tasks and functions. Thus, the probabilities would appear quite small that a meaningful training program or job description could be designed for such a broad area. An analogy to the medical field seems appropriate here. No one is trained as a "paramedical worker" and no job is so labeled. This is, however, a useful aggregate term for categorizing a large number of fields, jobs, and persons for descriptive convenience. Training is not designed for this gross level of description. The types of persons and positions that fall into this category, such as X-ray technician, laboratory technician, physical therapist, nurse's aide, etc., are dealt with as entities. Each field has different educational background requirements and presents different types and lengths of training to persons who will perform quite different duties.

It is of course true that to a very great extent the distinctions among these latter job classifications, the duties performed, and their unique training programs evolved from an articulated technological base. As we have previously indicated, such is not the case in the mental health area. Despite this, it would appear that increased semantic and conceptual precision is still possible. Thus, for example, specification of target populations (the aged, the mentally retarded, alcoholics, etc.) for which new jobs and roles are needed would offer some hope for greater clarification and ultimately greater precision in manpower requirements. By focusing on definitive population groups, training programs can be designed on the basis of services and function to be provided, and the types of persons, educational background, didactic materials, practicum experience, and physical settings can be established that are optimum to serve these ends.

A society can set its goals as it will, and spend what it will to accomplish them, but it must also balance out the advantages of trying to reach these goals against all the efforts required to attain them (Fein, 1967). The problems of crime, delinquency, alcoholism, drug abuse, poverty, aging, and other such current concerns are the products of a social value system—not a cause but an effect. Acceptance or rejection of these values as well as the methods chosen to implement social change are rarely based on scientific study and research. Rather, they come to be on the basis of social validation (LaPiere, 1959), which is the institutionalization of still other beliefs, opinions, and values.

Still, we must apply what knowledge we possess to assess current assumptions and practices and the "givens" that underlie much of our traditional patterns of service, care, and treatment. We must come to grips with the discrepancies that exist between our concepts of need (the ideal state) and the realistic probabilities of attainment. Alternative models and plans must be explored, not merely old labels applied as new solutions to old problems. Professional concern must be directed to all these issues so as to protect the people we wish to train from failure and disillusionment. Similarly, we must protect the population from being promised a great increase in "service" when in reality they may be "served" by someone with little knowledge or skill, whose job was created primarily as a means of relieving unemployment.

REFERENCES

ABEL-SMITH, B., and R. M. TITMUS. 1956. *The cost of the National Health Service.* Cambridge: Cambridge University Press.

ALBEE, G. W. 1959. *Mental health manpower trends.* New York: Basic Books.

ARNHOFF, F. N. 1966. Review of F. J. Kobler, *Casebook in psychopathology. Contemporary Psychology,* 11:230–232.

———. 1968. Realities and mental health manpower. *Mental Hygiene,* 52:181–189.

BRILL, N. Q., and H. A. STORROW. VTFJ. Social class and psychiatric treatment. *Archives of General Psychiatry,* 3:340–344.

DUBOS, R. 1959. *Mirage of health.* New York: Anchor Books.

EYSENCK, H. J. 1966. *The effects of psychotherapy.* New York: International Science Press.

FEIN, R. 1967. *The doctor shortage: an economic diagnosis.* Washington, D.C.: Brookings Institution.

GOLDBERG, G. S. New nonprofessionals in the human services: an overview. Paper presented at the Conference on the Use of Nonprofessionals in Mental Health Work, Washington, D.C., May, 1967.

GOLDHAMMER, H., and A. W. MARSHALL. 1953. *Psychosis and civilization.* Glencoe, Ill.: The Free Press.

GURIN, G., J. VEROFF, and S. FELD. 1960. *Americans view their mental health.* New York: Basic Books.

HOLLINGSHEAD, A. B., and F. C. REDLICH. 1958. *Social class and mental illness.* New York: Wiley.

IMBER, S. D., E. H. NASH, JR., and A. R. STONE. 1955. Social class and duration of psychotherapy. *Journal of Clinical Psychology,* 11:281–284.

Joint Commission on Mental Illness and Health. 1961. *Action for mental health.* New York: Basic Books.

KRAMER, M. 1966. *Some implications of trends in the usage of public facilities for community mental health programs and related research.* Public Health Service Publication No. 1434. Washington, D.C.: U.S. Government Printing Office.

LaPIERE, P. 1959. *The Freudian ethic.* New York: Duell, Sloan, and Pearce.

LEVINE, R. A. 1964. Treatment in the home: an experiment with low-income multi-problem families. In F. Reissman, J. Cohen, and A. Pearl (Eds.), *Mental health of the poor.* New York: Free Press of Glencoe.

McMAHON, J. T. 1964. The working class psychiatric patient: a clinical view. In F. Reissman, J. Cohen, and A. Pearl (Eds.), *Mental health of the poor.* New York: Free Press of Glencoe.

MASSIMO, J. L., and M. F. SHORE. 1963. The effectiveness of a comprehensive, vocationally oriented psychotherapeutic program for adolescent delinquent boys. *American Journal of Orthopsychiatry,* 33:634–642.

MENCHER, S. Social trends, social policy and manpower. Paper presented at the Institute on Research Approaches to Manpower Problems in Social Welfare Services to Children and Families, University of Minnesota, Duluth Campus, August, 1964.

MILLER, S. M., and E. G. MISHLER. 1959. Social class, mental illness, and American psychiatry: an expository review. *Milbank Memorial Fund Quarterly,* 37 (2) : 174–199.

National Commission on Technology, Automation and Economic Progress. 1966. *Technology and the American economy.* Vol. 1. Washington, D.C.: U.S. Government Printing Office.

National Institute of Mental Health, Division of Manpower and Training Programs. 1967. *Mental health training and manpower, 1968–1972.* Chevy Chase, Md.: NIMH.

OVERALL, B., and H. ARONSON. 1963. Expectations of psychotherapy in patients of lower socioeconomic class. *American Journal of Orthopsychiatry,* 33:421–430.

PEARL, A., and F. REISSMAN (Eds.) . 1965. *New careers for the poor: the nonprofessional in human service.* New York: Free Press of Glencoe.

RYAN, W. 1967. *Distress in the city: a summary report of the Boston Mental Health Survey (1960–1962).* Boston: Massachusetts Association for Mental Health, Massachusetts Department of Mental Health, and United Community Services of Metropolitan Boston.

Southern Regional Education Board. 1966. *The community college in mental health training.* Report of a conference, Atlanta, April.

STURM, H. M. 1967. Technological developments and their effects upon health manpower. *Monthly Labor Review,* 90:1–8.

THUMIN, F. J., and M. ZEBELMAN. 1967. Psychology vs. psychiatry: a study of public image. *American Psychologist,* 22:282–286.

CHAPTER 9

Utilization of Manpower
in Provision of
Mental Health Services

ALAN D. MILLER AND PHILIP WEXLER

"THE UNDENIABLE FACT is that the gap be-
tween manpower needs and the supply of trained personnel is too great
to be closed. It will grow much worse before it gets better" (National
Health Forum, 1957, pp. 107–108).

Although this statement dates back to a discussion of mental health
manpower held at the National Health Forum in 1957, it remains as
timely today as it was then. Along with similar expressions of concern
over serious shortages of all types of mental health personnel voiced repeatedly over the past two decades, it is evident that we have not suddenly
awakened to an unforeseen or previously nonexistent problem.

A wide variety of recommendations and proposals concerned with the
alleviation of manpower shortages and the more effective use of personnel
may be found in mental health and other relevant literature. Obviously,
many professional groups and individuals have given a great deal of

thought over a long period of time to finding ways of overcoming problems created by critical manpower shortages. What is most distressing about these recommendations is that many are just as pertinent today as they were as long as twenty years ago.

Some of the solutions that have been proposed would require profound changes in the way in which this nation approaches its social and economic problems and the underlying factors that determine our goals and value systems. Some recommendations are nothing more than poorly conceived schemes that, if attempted, might do more harm than good. However, many, perhaps the majority, are well-formulated, carefully considered suggestions that would appear to lend themselves to implementation without any major disruptions in the organization and administration of present mental health services, and, in any event, are worth trying.

It is in respect to this latter group that we raise the following questions: Why have apparently sound, worthwhile recommendations failed to produce the anticipated benefits or solutions to our manpower problems? Why has there been no definitive action taken in connection with so many proposals that appear both promising and workable or are at least deserving of an opportunity to be tried out?

It is our thesis that failure or lack of action results from the perpetuation of a number of conditions that confront us whenever we attempt to deal with our manpower problems.

Clearly, one of the greatest difficulties standing in the way of providing needed services is lack of trained manpower. It is equally clear, however, that the reality of the situation forces us to concentrate on meeting manpower needs by defining the problem as effective use of people instead of numbers. We propose to review some of the recommendations related to the use of mental health personnel that have been and continue to be made most frequently, and to attempt to identify the major reasons for failure or lack of definitive action. We further propose to suggest positive steps that we believe must be taken in order to bring about any significant improvements in the mental health manpower situation.

A review of some of the numerous recommendations and proposals concerning effective use of manpower will help set the stage for the identification of major barriers that seem to be obstructing their implementation.

A search of the literature for such recommendations conducted for the California Department of Mental Hygiene (1965) produced 41 frequently cited suggestions. In another recent report, Lockman (1966) classified 120 actual and proposed solutions, both comprehensive and general, into four categories.

I

Our own approach, borrowing somewhat from the above sources, suggests eight categories, the first seven dealing with recommendations and proposals related primarily to the setting in which service is provided and work performed, the last with the individual and factors that either block or promote his entry into mental health-related professions or occupations. All are interrelated, so that duplication and overlapping cannot be avoided.

1. *Improving the effectiveness of the user of manpower—the managerial system.* Recommendations concerned with the effectiveness of the organization as a management system cover a wide range. We are told that it is first of all essential to orient management to value better use of staff from the top down. It is equally important, we are advised, to take a broad view aimed at finding fundamental solutions to our basic problems rather than a fragmented approach resulting at best in piecemeal solutions to isolated problems. Long-range policy-planning, modeling, and systems study are all aspects of this approach. Economic, social, and political value systems are involved. Specific proposals in this grouping are related to unused capacity, leadership and supervision, communications, planning, cost-analysis studies, working conditions, labor relations, training, studies of alternative methods, designing measures of productivity and evaluation, and the use of electronic data-processing.

2. *Assuring that there is a reasonable match between skills available and jobs to be performed.* Involved here are recommendations concerned with job study. We are urged to study and analyze the nature, quality, and quantity of the work performed by those we employ, how their functions interrelate, to what extent their training is used, and to what degree they function at their maximum capacity for the greatest percentage of the time. It is suggested that job clusters be defined so that job-ladder training bases can be built.

There are numerous references in this group to recruitment and employment, work assignments and groupings, job design and redesign, and skill-acquisition patterns. Suggestions in regard to the use of part-time volunteer workers and where to recruit them appear frequently.

In general, it is suggested that the work to be performed and the skills required for specific jobs be clearly defined and identified. Jobs can be changed to meet our needs, and workers helped to acquire new or modified skills through training. Better use of available people can thus be facilitated by redesigning the match between skills and jobs.

3. *Orienting services to changing concepts of care and treatment.* Recommendations in this category stress the importance of keeping up with advances and new developments in preventive, screening, diagnostic,

therapeutic, and rehabilitative techniques and methods, as well as changes in the settings in which these services are provided.

Implied here is the belief that timely application of technological advances might either decrease the demand for particular types of personnel or lead to changes in their roles and functions, thus enabling them to make more effective use of their time and to provide expanded service to an extended population.

The establishment and use of new types of supportive personnel to provide direct assistance to the professional, and in some situations to provide forms of help the professional cannot offer, is a recommendation that is widely promoted, as is the use of the team or task-force approach in the provision of services.

4. *Research and studies related to education, career choice, and career patterns.* Under this heading a variety of proposals has been made urging more careful study of: educational programs, career choice and career patterns; the relationship of findings made in these areas to the availability and distribution of manpower; and the use of skills in the provision of services.

Specific recommendations are often presented in regard to measures to increase the supply of manpower, to motivate for choice of health careers, and to affect preemployment education so that interdisciplinary teams are better prepared to work together with maximum effectiveness.

Emphasis is placed on the importance of providing opportunities for training so as to make possible the upgrading of personnel as they acquire new skills. This has been referred to as the "cascading training concept," by means of which persons with little or no preparation for the work required are brought into the organization, trained, and promoted to positions of greater responsibility, thus helping to assure the introduction of a continuing supply of manpower into the system. In connection with recommendations of this type, we are urged to take advantage of various federal training-grant funds available for this purpose.

5. *Analyzing inventories and surveys as a basis for planning for the effective use of manpower.* It is frequently recommended that we develop methods to improve our ability to conduct ongoing inventories and surveys by means of which information in respect to the supply of and demand for mental health personnel, geographic distribution, and the availability of needed skills can be systematically obtained. A regular flow of this kind of information and a thorough analysis of the implications it might contain are seen as essential bases for planning for the effective use of existing manpower, as well as for forecasting future needs.

6. *The quantity approaches to meeting manpower needs.* A great many recommendations have been made that can generally be referred to as ways of quantitatively improving both the supply and the productivity

of manpower. Recommendations of this type appear in nearly all group-ings into which proposals have been classified. For example, the use of untapped manpower sources, including part-time employees and volunteers, represents a suggested means of increasing the total supply. Increasing productivity is represented by suggestions for ways and means of freeing fully trained professionals to spend more time in actual treatment and to help assure that more people who need service can obtain it.

7. *Using experimental and developmental patterns to clear the path ahead.* In this group may be included various recommendations generally concerned with experimentation and the testing out of new patterns of organizing and delivering service. This type of recommendation also appears in several of the previous categories.

As proposals for action, they call for the formulation of adequate research designs to develop models for studying manpower performance in various types of settings, or to test hypotheses related to manpower problems and their proposed solution by means of demonstration and pilot projects. For example, there is a widely held assumption that individuals with less than complete professional training can serve an important role in mental health programs. There are, however, too few opportunities to test this assumption extensively so as to change it from an unsubstantiated belief to a manpower principle that can be effectively applied.

8. *Influencing the character and quality of basic preparation, educational opportunity, and career counseling.* Recommendations in this category range from those calling for the redesign of the nation's educational system, the quality of which is said to be declining, to proposals aimed at preventing the waste of our human resources.

The strengthening of curricula at all educational levels, the obligation to create the conditions under which the individual's potentialities may be realized, the need for early identification of skills and talents, better school guidance and vocational counseling programs, and increased educational opportunity for minority groups are among the many areas in which various recommendations have been made.

II

With the preceding summary of manpower recommendations and proposals as background, we turn next to an examination of the conditions that in our opinion serve to obstruct their effective implementation.

These conditions cover a broad range of philosophical, procedural, and policy-related concerns. They are related to ways in which groups and individuals function in our society and, more specifically in our own area of interest, to the organizational and administrative policies and practices that govern our present-day mental health programs. They also involve the internal and external forces that influence both the goals we establish and the means we use in attempting to achieve them.

Those we have selected for closer attention have been singled out because we believe there can be no significant improvements in our manpower situation without their removal or modification.

Perpetuation of Goals

It is a truism that today's big business, industrial organizations, and government agencies cannot live without a continuing flow of innovations, but it is also clearly evident that they cannot live well with them or readily respond to them.

Studies of government agencies reveal them to be self-maintaining and self-reinforcing systems of communication and control. They are constituted to maintain a "steady state," to go on being just what they are and doing very much what they have been doing. While they tend to welcome innovation in theory, they often ignore or resist it in practice. This should not be viewed as a matter of hypocrisy but rather a characteristic of the very nature of these organizations. They are usually well organized to deal with what is known or with what can be safely and easily inferred from it. The unknown, the uncertain, and the unpredictable make them unsure and fearful. The more radical the innovation, the more likely it is to produce intolerable anxiety in many individuals and organizations, and the more strongly it will be resisted.

Perpetuation of Structure

The presence of archaic and inefficient government-agency administrative structures, together with a proliferation of governmental activity in mental health and related services, has resulted in serious problems in decision-making and the coordination of public programs. This has also contributed to the wide disparities that exist between available financial resources and community and human needs, and it has led as well to a reduction in public accountability.

Perpetuation of Method

The present organization of systems of providing care and treatment is by and large inadequate and was not designed to provide care and treatment in the modern sense. State mental hospitals were designed for long-term institutionalization. Mental health clinics too frequently follow the private-practice model and operate with a selectivity that often excludes those in greatest need of treatment.

Perpetuation of Occupations and Skills

The increasing professionalism of mental health workers constitutes a particularly serious obstacle to more effective use of mental health man-power. The more training and experience it takes to produce the various types of professionals needed, the more they tend to become oriented around professional standards and approaches; from this follows gaps in communication and understanding and intergroup status conflicts.

The promotion of higher professional standards is an important ele-ment for the preparation and practice of a profession. However, as Ginzberg (1966) has said:

Any service for human beings must inevitably be concerned with quality, but it must not be concerned with quality in such a way that it blocks itself. Of course, we are interested in teachers and ministers and nurses and physicians who are capable. But there is no reason for a large industry to establish unnecessarily high standards.

The most serious barrier to effective manpower utilization in the health field that I see is the fact that each group is not strong enough to fight successfully against the group which is higher on the ladder and which spends most of its energy preventing those below from moving up. The struggle for social prestige and market power between physicians and nurses, and the nurses and the tech-nicians, the technicians and the practical nurses or auxiliary nurses, etc., makes any rational, long-term policy for manpower utilization so difficult to realize (p. 18).

Some passing references to the dynamics of perpetuation are also in order. A detailed analysis will not be attempted, but the following state-ments represent a line of thought about some of the factors that support perpetuation.

1. The energy and work required simply to maintain the status quo usually exhaust initiative in an organization; in the interest of economy of effort, actual resistance to change often follows.

2. The activities of every day are the most effective teacher, and, hence, practices tend to perpetuate themselves and train others who use them to continue in the same mode. Closely related are structured sets of tasks that also reduce opportunities to learn other ways.

3. Our purposes as an agency may be at cross-purposes with other agencies and our values may be competing with other values. For ex-ample, the relative importance of health services and education programs is a matter for discussion in regard to distribution of resources. The out-come of such discussions influences the level of support to the involved agencies.

4. There also may be competition among values at a higher, more ab-stract level: i.e., individual initiative to solve problems versus govern-mental responsibility; economy versus expenditures; state versus local.

5. In any change, however progressive, there is a cost to some. There are those who lose out in any change, and they may be expected to resist the change.

Having reviewed some of the most frequently cited manpower recommendations, followed by identification of some of the major reasons for failure or lack of definitive action to implement them, our attention is focused next on the formulation of guidelines to a course of action to improve the mental health manpower situation.

How can a state agency with broad responsibility for the development and administration of statewide comprehensive mental health and mental retardation services best deal with the factors that support the perpetuation of conditions previously outlined? What can be done to strengthen our ability to meet overall manpower needs?

New York State's mental hygiene program represents perhaps the largest and most complex state-government operation in the world, requiring the services of over 50,000 persons. The Department of Mental Hygiene operates 31 institutions, including nineteen hospitals for the mentally ill, ten schools for the retarded, a research and training institute, and a hospital for short-term treatment and training. The department also administers an extensive state-aided community mental health program and a wide variety of specialized services and activities.

The section that follows is based on steps that have been taken within this setting. The suggestions we offer represent measures related to agency organization and the introduction of programs designed to enable the Department of Mental Hygiene to deal more effectively with specific problems involving particular areas of special concern. Included also are recommendations and observations that are more generalized in nature and might be better classified as basic principles underlying the determination of policy and the approaches we take.

1. *Organizational measures to strengthen ability to meet overall manpower needs.*

In respect to promoting the more effective use of manpower, an essential and seemingly obvious first step is to improve the effectiveness of the organizational and managerial system of the user of manpower.

Although this step seems an obvious one, it is frequently bypassed or ignored by mental health agencies, which too often continue to use outdated approaches and procedures, and fail to organize themselves so that they can think and act on a scale equal to the problem.

The need for a stronger overall organization ties in with the simple need for a greater degree of strength and competence to overcome entropy. In addition, there must be a number of deliberately incorporated correctives and stimulants to counteract the natural tendency for any agency to deteriorate. Measures that may be instituted along these lines can result in an organizational structure that will necessitate interaction and cooperation among the various operating divisions. They may interact competitively, but, in any event, interaction will occur.

Recognition of the need for this essential first step was evidenced in the reorganization of the Central Office of the New York State Department of Mental Hygiene.

The development of statewide comprehensive mental health and mental retardation services requires departmental implementation of major new concepts of treatment and rehabilitation, a new emphasis on regional planning and local responsibility, and an extensively broadened involvement in education, training, and research activities, all of which involves a vast increase in the scope, complexity, and sophistication of programs to be administered by the Central Office.

It was virtually self-evident that a stronger and more fully developed organizational structure was needed to strengthen the capacity of the department's Central Office to meet these responsibilities. This was the basis for the major reorganization that was effected.

From our point of view, an extremely significant component of the reorganization plan is the Office of Manpower and Training. This organizational unit, with the capability to devote its full attention to a broad range of manpower matters, was established to provide top-level direction and coordination of essential personnel, education, and training programs. The following list of functional statements outlines its major responsibilities:

(1) Administers the department's personnel program, including recruitment, manpower planning, salary and job classification, employee services, and employee relations.

(2) Directs a comprehensive program of education and training, both formal and inservice, for professional and nonprofessional personnel.

(3) Supervises and coordinates staff and management development.

(4) Directs a program for professional recruitment.

(5) Administers the department's program for the development and use of volunteer services.

(6) Represents the department in developing and maintaining relationships with professional groups.

The presence of this office has clearly established a strong focal point for departmental concern and action in respect to manpower problems and their attempted solutions.

2. Organizational measures to strengthen planning and coordination functions and responsibilities.

Many of the recommendations we have reviewed stress the importance of program planning and coordination. It is pointed out frequently that manpower problems cannot be dealt with outside the context of consideration of overall agency goals and the means used in attempting to achieve them.

No agency can fulfill all of its aspirations at the same time. Competing claims must be balanced and conscious choices made. As indicated earlier, the increasing complexity and proliferation of governmental activity in mental health and related services have resulted in serious problems in decision-making and the coordination of programs. Although these problems are widely acknowledged, too few agencies have tried to develop their ability to deal with them.

While the department's philosophy might be said to be in keeping with Carlyle's familiar dictum, "Our main business is not to see what lies dimly at a distance, but to do what lies clearly at hand," there is clear recognition of the necessity for a mechanism that can help assure a continuing and comprehensive understanding of how critical decisions relate to existing policies and programs and to all present and probable future development.

Since 1964 the State of New York has been attempting to cope more effectively with the increasing complexities of government through the development of a Programming-Planning-Budgeting System (PPBS), which systematically relates the expenditure of funds to the accomplishment of planned goals.

PPBS treats the entire operational structure of state government as an integrated system directed toward the fulfillment of a great variety of governmental goals established to meet state needs. After these objectives are identified and governmental activities related to them, specific expenditures can be assessed in terms of achievement of planned goals.

To relate the department's planning activities to the state system and at the same time provide for coordination of the development, evaluation, revision, and implementation of all long-range program-planning involving federal, state, and community agencies, the Office of Program Planning and Coordination was established under the department's reorganization plan.

Among the major functions of this office, in line with top-level commitment to the planning process, are:

(1) Initiating, coordinating, and/or participating in the program-planning activities of units of the department.

(2) Assisting in coordination of the planning, development, and implementation of comprehensive prevention, treatment, and rehabilitation services in mental health and mental retardation carried on by federal, state, and local departments and agencies and professional organizations and citizens' groups.

(3) Coordination of departmental participation on interagency com-

mittees working on mental health, mental retardation, and related programs.

In outlining our own efforts in this area, our purpose is to emphasize the importance of an unqualified commitment to planning as an ongoing agency responsibility. While planning as a term has become familiar and popular, the process often consists of not much more than an exercise that has little chance of success because it is unrelated to the reality of the situation, is based on insufficient or inaccurate facts, or is carried out in isolation from the setting in which problems exist or issues must be resolved.

Since the resolution of many of the issues in the manpower field undoubtedly will require changes in the way in which services are provided, as well as the manner in which people function, there must be serious consideration given to the relationship between planning efforts and desired changes.

The inevitability of change necessitates continuity of planning, so that adjustments to it become part of the process. Moreover, planning itself must be viewed as an agent for change, so that a serious commitment to planning must also carry with it a readiness to anticipate change and an understanding that it can also facilitate change.

3. *Communications.*

Problems in communication have been blamed for failures and inefficiency in all areas of agency operation. Much has been written and said about breakdowns in communication and how they can be prevented. While we are concerned with the improvement and strengthening of policies and methods involving the sharing of information, our major concern is with a broader concept of communication, which includes all of the processes by means of which people influence one another.

Communication in this sense has as its main objective the promotion of mutual understanding and does not refer solely to the transmittal of messages.

Our approach to the development of a systematic two-way flow of information requires that equal attention be given to both the seeking out of information and its dissemination.

Using manpower programs as a case in point, we consider it of vital importance to disseminate, both within and beyond the boundaries of the agency's network of services, a steady flow of information concerning policies and developments directly or indirectly related to a broad range of personnel, education, and training matters.

However, important as it is, we see the transmittal of information as only one aspect of the communication process. To our way of thinking, the successful implementation of manpower programs and the resolution of issues that have a bearing on them require the cultivation of independent critics who will react to what we do or propose. It is essential that the flow of information outward be countered by an input of ideas, suggestions, and criticism from employee groups, professional associations, those responsible for education and training, and the general public. This means that our decentralized operations must be planned, not only to carry out activities with maximum effectiveness, but also to provide us with a sensory mechanism. To further assure that we will hear from those whose criticism and thinking is important to us, we must include in our planning those measures designed to strengthen employee groups, voluntary associations, and volunteer programs. While the use of volunteers is recommended as a means of alleviating manpower shortages, we must learn to take advantage of the fact that they also represent a highly personalized and extremely valuable segment of our two-way communications system.

If we want the values served by our organization to be clearly understood, it follows that there must be a strengthening of the activities through which we attempt to gain public understanding of the issues involved. This means that the public must be made aware of the consequences of carrying out certain programs and also the cost to it if a program is not carried out. In the public relations effort required, we must be prepared to be scrupulously honest rather than polemic. In this connection, observation and evaluation are essential in providing an accurate basis for reporting to the public.

It should also be noted that this approach helps to make experimentation more comfortable—an important consideration as we deliberately plan for experimentation and in fact make it obligatory.

4. The facilitation of career development.

Many occupations are required to provide adequate mental health services, and there are differing periods of education and training needed to enter and advance in these occupations. It is a well-established fact that opportunities and incentives for advancement are closely related to the success or failure of recruitment and have an important bearing on turnover rates. Upgrading of personnel already employed is the most efficient method of getting the next higher level of technical aid and the quickest way to open up entry-level jobs for recruits.

In order to make fuller use of the skill potentials of our employees, to provide them with incentives to make their maximum contribution, and to attract new workers in greater numbers, the New York State Department of Mental Hygiene recently instituted the first phase of a new career-ladder plan. The concept is by no means new, but its implementation represents a significant step forward.

It is referred to here to illustrate the complex changes that must occur for a seemingly simple plan to be implemented. In brief, the career-ladder plan emphasizes employment opportunities for a variety of individuals, from those with a minimal educational background to others who have completed two- or four-year college programs with or without special preparation for mental health or related occupations. Stress is placed on training built into the job, with added education provided through enrollment in part-time or full-time college or university courses of study.

To fit this type of program into the personnel system of a government agency so that not only jobs but also careers can be created requires planning and action to assure the establishment of the necessary conditions, while at the same time modifying or removing others that stand in the way. Jobs must be redefined and the job structure reorganized to allow new hierarchical levels from job entry up to the fully professionalized position. This calls for changes in the table of organization and a redefinition of both nonprofessional and professional jobs. There must be recognition that meaningful work can be satisfactorily performed by persons other than those who have had many years of education and highly specialized training. There must also be support available to enable those with ability and aptitude to return to school, thus making possible advancement on the basis of experience, on-the-job training, and formal education.

As a further illustration of the kind of cooperative action necessary, the introduction of the career-ladder plan into the New York system could not have been accomplished without the understanding and support of the State Department of Civil Service, the State Division of the Budget, and the legislature. Legislation authorizing the Department of Mental Hygiene to grant educational leave with pay has been one of the key factors in the facilitation of the plan.

Our main purpose in describing the career-ladder plan is to stress the extreme importance and urgency of establishing career-development programs and opportunities. There are many other aspects of career development that must be considered in the organization of an agency-wide approach open to all employees.

For example, provision should be made for employee mobility within the system, not only vertically, but horizontally as well. Supervisory lines should be planned deliberately so that there will be a scramble of traditional relationships. As an illustration, members of one profession might supervise members of another, or supervision might be assigned without reference to profession. Similarly, training sessions must be planned so that there is some deliberate experimentation.

A career-development program should also include some provision for periodic escape, through either educational leave or some type of sabbatical absence. Sabbatical leave need not be for a year; it may be for a week or a month. Another form of escape that has received increasing attention recently is the exchange of personnel between local, state, and federal public and private agencies.

5. *Agency responsibility.*

If there is any single major point to be emphasized in reviewing the suggestions we have offered, it is that there must be an explicit and unreserved assumption of responsibility on the part of the mental health agency for active participation in all aspects of programs designed to deal with manpower problems.

It is our contention that government agencies have an immense responsibility to strive constantly for improvement in the quality and effectiveness of programs and services they administer.

Assumption of such responsibility takes various forms and contains many implications. It implies above all the promotion of unity of purpose. It suggests initiation of activity rather than passive acceptance of conditions that block reform and innovation: the ability to act rather than simply to react. It makes obligatory a continuing examination and evaluation of the aims and conduct of the organization, including its philosophy, policies, objectives, and programs.

It must stress the development of collaborative efforts as opposed to competition. To help assure successful achievement of its goals, an agency must learn to operate, not solely on its own, but in cooperation with a host of related agencies and organizations.

In respect to the inevitability of change, whether stimulated from within or imposed from the outside, we must be very much aware of those who stand to lose by it. For example, changes in either our own organization or in professions whose skills we require affect those who have been taught in the past. They continue to use outdated techniques and outmoded methods and do not know how to function in newer ways. We have an urgent obligation to train our staff, especially those in the mental health professions, so that they can change and learn new skills and competencies. If we can succeed in doing this, we will have eliminated a major source of resistance to change, and we will have done so in the most constructive way possible. If we fail to do it, we must anticipate that change will lead not only to inefficiency but to resistance as well.

We must also recognize that in programs such as ours, the cost of change in human terms might in some instances be too high. We cannot afford, as in private industry, to be ruthless. Organizational measures through which change is often brought about must be viewed as narrowly and incompletely formulated if more people are hurt than helped by such change.

To choose a categorical example, if we could find a way of treatment of all of the patients in our hospitals in half the time it now takes by using an electronic machine that made 90 per cent of our present staff obsolete, we would have to give serious thought to how this development should be implemented. At a more likely level, we cannot ignore the effect a campaign to reduce the size of our institutions may have on certain communities that have depended entirely on us. Without implying that our patients would be penalized, we must be aware of and take responsibility for the price of change.

We firmly believe that the assumption of responsibility by an agency and its staff can be promoted by the measures we have described, and we recognize that the character of original training, as well as daily experience, will provide the initial impetus.

6. *Education and training.*

Our consideration of manpower problems would be incomplete if we omitted a summary of some of our views concerning education and training.

Recent years have witnessed many changes in our mental health programs. New types of services have been developed. There has been a significant increase in the willingness and readiness of mental health professionals to face problems in new ways and an encouraging growth in the acceptance of new ideas. Perhaps most important, new people have been brought into the field. These have been positive factors for promoting the growth and renewal of our organizations, and efforts to stimulate them must be continuous.

We have referred previously to the need to seek such stimulation in the form of ideas, suggestions, and criticism from outside our organization. We must also take steps to assure it from within the organization, and, in this connection, the manner in which we view and carry out our responsibilities in relation to education and training is of critical importance.

While it has been widely acknowledged that well-planned training programs for all categories of personnel are essential to satisfactory initial placement and to the fullest use of available people, in general this represents a concern for immediate training needs rather than a responsibility for basic education. Although mental health agencies often complain that academic training too frequently is unrelated to the needs and realities of the work to be performed, they seldom attempt to influence its nature and character.

From our point of view, agencies must assume responsibility for initiating serious partnerships and close working relationships with colleges, universities, medical schools, and a wide variety of training centers. Affiliations with such facilities must be actively sought, and, when established, should stress the mutual benefits to be derived from working together.

While academic centers have responsibility for curricula, teaching methods, and instructional materials, agencies should not be reluctant to undertake critical review and offer suggestions for revising and strengthening program content and methods.

In our agencies we are looking for people who can bring to us not only up-to-date knowledge and professional competency but, perhaps even more important, the skills and ability to work cooperatively with others, professionals and nonprofessionals alike. We need those who can contribute to our efforts to innovate, experiment, plan, and evaluate. To help develop such individuals, we must influence, convince, and persuade those responsible for providing professional preparation to design their programs to meet our needs more effectively.

In return, as public service agencies, we should be prepared to provide service bases in which specific job skills and technical knowledge can be acquired and practiced by students and trainees. To this end, our service settings must represent the best possible models we can design.

Finally, we must aggressively solicit financial support for both trainees and training programs. Mental health agency expenditures for this purpose have been minimal in comparison with our needs. It is imperative that qualified candidates receive financial assistance to enable them to complete their training, and that training centers be supported so that their programs may be expanded and strengthened.

IV

Our suggestions, recommendations, and observations may be summarized as follows:

1. Capability to devote top-level, full-time attention to a broad range of manpower matters is a critical need of agencies responsible for the provision of mental health services. As an essential first step in promoting the more effective use of mental health manpower, it is strongly recommended that every major mental health agency, especially those whose functions are statewide in scope, establish an organizational and administrative mechanism designed to assume responsibility for dealing with manpower problems at all levels of agency operation.

2. Organizational measures to strengthen manpower programs require concurrent measures to strengthen planning and coordination functions.

3. A broad concept of communications, with emphasis on the development of a systematic two-way flow of information and having as its main objective the promotion of mutual understanding, must be built into the organization and consistently fostered, not only through the mass media, but also on an interpersonal basis wherever possible.

4. No plan for improving the utilization of mental health manpower can be complete without acceptance of career development as a core concept underlying the design and operation of all agency programs.

5. In the final analysis, staff strength and, in turn, agency effectiveness grow out of the assumption of responsibility for purposeful activity rather

than out of knowledge of specific techniques and the possession of special skills. Planned, deliberate efforts for open acknowledgment of this concept should be included in the formulation of all agency policies and programs.

6. Mental health agencies should take the initiative in establishing affiliations and close working relationships with the academic centers responsible for basic education. Furthermore, they should make every effort to influence the character and quality of professional preparation, so that it becomes more closely aligned with public service needs.

It should be emphasized that we have not intended to provide a final blueprint that, if followed, will assure the solution of our problems. Positive prescription is difficult; complex manpower problems do not lend themselves to simple solutions.

In general, we have stressed organizational measures that are largely centralized in role and function, though not completely. However, we have tried to present them so that they reflect a point of view, a way of thinking and acting in respect to manpower problems that we believe must permeate our mental health system.

In recommending organizational measures, we are very much aware that they do not always solve the basic underlying problems we face, but only restructure and redirect our approaches to their solution. If our planning and strategy have been wrong, we recognize that we may be creating in new forms the very conditions we are attempting to modify or remove. If we have been correct, our effectiveness will be increased. We must be alert to the danger that an organizational unit starting out with a focused concern eventually may become just another compartment competing for scarce attention and resources.

We have also emphasized the assumption of responsibility and initiative because, abstract though these terms may be, the manner in which they are interpreted and applied often will make the difference between success and failure in the approaches we take.

Finally, we have tried not to lose sight of the human element—the individual and his problems, needs, and aspirations; not to forget that while our main mission is to treat and rehabilitate the mentally disabled, we also have responsibility and concern for those who are employed to perform the essential tasks involved in providing these services.

REFERENCES

California Department of Mental Hygiene. 1965. *Mental health manpower: an annotated bibliography and commentary.* Vol 1. Sacramento: California Medical Education and Research Foundation.

GINZBERG, E. 1966. Manpower in a service economy. In *Training health service workers: the critical challenge.* Proceedings of the Conference on Job Development and Training for Workers in Health Services, February 1966. Washington, D.C.: U.S. Government Printing Office.

LOCKMAN, R. F. 1966. *Concepts and proposals for improving manpower utilization in mental health.* Mental Health Manpower Current Statistical and Activities Report No. 11. Chevy Chase, Md.: NIMH.

National Health Forum. 1957. *Better mental health.* New York: National Health Council.

CHAPTER 10

Summary and Conclusions

FRANKLYN N. ARNHOFF AND
JOSEPH C. SPEISMAN

THE PREVIOUS CHAPTERS have presented, in depth, discussions of some of the major contextual dimensions along which manpower issues unfold. This chapter will highlight some of the most cogent points, drawing heavily upon the formal discussions and comments in the symposium itself.

Despite the wide divergence in the topics of the formal papers as well as in the interests and backgrounds of the participants, the convergence of discussion and the interrelatedness of concepts and positions were rather remarkable. To a great extent this occurred because the issues of mental health manpower have not received the same comprehensive treatment as have health issues in general. The voluminous literature on health manpower, health economics, and the politics of health has received inadequate translation to mental health problems. Since many of the participants have extensive knowledge and experience in the broader fields, mental health and illness considerations could readily be viewed as special instances of general health principles. Although cultural and social issues play a major role in all health conceptualizations, they are, however, of even greater importance when one turns to consideration of human behavior, which is a basic focus for mental health.

Consequently, much of the discussion focused upon the ideological conceptualizations of modern American society: the latent issues upon which current and future efforts in health, education, and welfare must be based. There was not, nor can there be, any meaningful discourse on manpower issues divorced from this aggregate view of total society and its economic and political realities.

Despite an emphasis upon theoretical orientation in the choice of formal papers and participants, it became apparent almost immediately that there were two general classes of comment in the discussion. The first were the theoretical conceptions of the major social, economic, and political factors that not only influence and determine manpower issues but also are essential to provide a clear understanding of the fundamental conceptualizations of manpower. The second theme to emerge in the discussion was presented from the practical and pragmatic point of view and represented the state and federal agencies that are concerned principally with direct and immediate responsibility for manpower in the delivery of services.

While these themes are presented here as polarities, there was considerable overlap, and there was neither disdain nor disinterest expressed for either concern. The discussions reflected the desire of the participants to understand the mechanisms whereby theory, knowledge, and change could be translated into action through the media of practical politics and economics. Any actual polarization of points of view that was expressed in the discussion probably reflects the fundamental distinction between one who is charged with the responsibility to implement policy and the theoretician or observer, who may, perhaps, also advise.

In mental health, and perhaps in the health fields in general, there has been an overemphasis both on the numbers of people needed or produced to date and on the dollars spent or needed. There is no doubt that both are necessary, and the emphasis upon these two factors is extremely useful from the standpoint of practical politics and legislation. Both provide convenient, easily understood, concrete measures for program growth and development. However, the reliance on manpower statistics and upon dollars has reached an almost institutionalized status in the form of the relatively new and increasingly utilized Programming-Planning-Budgeting System (PPBS).[1]

PPBS, which received its greatest national attention via the Department of Defense, is now being implemented throughout the federal government and is becoming more prevalent in state and local government. The approach is quite utilitarian for the necessary strategies of the politics of budget increases and for the justification of programs by means of step-by-step pragmatic cost-accounting. However, as was repeatedly emphasized in discussion, the reliance upon PPBS for either the delineation or

---

1. See, for example, D. Novick (Ed.), *Program budgeting: Program analysis and the federal budget.* Cambridge, Mass.: Harvard University Press, 1965.

definition of goals is inappropriate, since such a system is largely a means of justifying growth but does not and cannot assure growth. Since manpower numbers and dollar amounts are primary data for such systematic approaches, this caveat is a major one. Sheer growth expressed in terms of manpower produced and dollars expended, divorced from a series of stated and measured objectives regarding program effectiveness, cannot either confirm or disconfirm causal relationships among manpower, costs, and mental health or illness. Thus, the justification for gross mental health manpower needs and budgets on the basis of growth potential alone is of limited utility. On the other hand, it was pointed out that the mental health field has been enormously successful without necessarily specifying manpower goals, by basing its arguments on the numbers that indicate the production of people, the dollars needed, and the progressive reduction of patient populations in the mental hospitals. It was concluded, however, that this approach was more appropriate in the early, formative stages of program establishment and development than it is at this time.

Another telling commentary on the limitations inherent in describing manpower by means of numbers alone was made by focusing on one of the key assumptions of the current mental health manpower approach. The assumption that a general increase in manpower would provide the necessary staff for specific programs has, in fact, not been borne out. For example, it was stated that the state hospitals are often more poorly staffed today than they were fifteen years ago. Thus, in effect, the people who have been supported in mental health training have not been specifically trained for direct employment in mental institutions or hospitals, and, therefore, while there have been huge increases in the numbers of people engaged in the total field, we have, in fact, failed to adequately staff the mental hospitals.

In fact, it has become less and less justifiable to think in terms of sheer manpower growth alone; rather, it appears increasingly appropriate to consider a dynamic change in the growth pattern whereby some established elements might well receive less support and be expected to decrease in numbers while others continue to grow and develop. A plea for much more qualitative analysis of the manpower question was repeatedly made, and it was emphasized that the specific naming of obtainable manpower objectives for particular purposes would aid in this endeavor.

Two elements emerged as particularly relevant to the programs of government and social agencies. One was the political approach to the attainment of budgets and the development of programs, and the second was the issue of the development of necessary professional manpower aside from the political implications. In effect, it was stated that a government agency must indeed be alert and responsive to the political implications of any action and certainly must provide the legislative authority with the materials in which that authority is interested. On the other hand, it was cautioned that any time a government agency based its actions and its substantive analyses on political values alone, there was a high probability that the programs of such an agency would become merely opportunistic and reactive, and probably doomed to mediocrity or failure.

Since budgetary processes, occupational attractiveness, educational support, and the entire mental health effort are intimately linked with politics and public policy, such considerations are paramount in any systematic approach to manpower. One of the most attractive and most readily agreed-upon propositions advanced during the discussion was that the formal decision processes of governments are based upon ideologies (overt or covert), and that it is essential to understand the referents of such ideologies. The aspect of ideological analysis that is important in the current framework entails an examination of the present and prospective objectives in the public health sector. In effect, the problem is stated to be an assessment of what can be accomplished, first, by invoking the layman's contemporary perspectives on these objectives and, second, by understanding the attempts to change public demands and expectations relating to mental health.

Lasswell has stated the following conditions, both present and prospective, regarding the ideology of health and illness: (1) the scope of behavior covered by the conception of mental illness has been enlarging; (2) the extent of this coverage is coming to a climax; (3) public programs explicitly justified in the name of mental health will gradually decline; and (4) the ideology of "cultural reconstruction" will increasingly guide the allocation of manpower resources, including the types of persons involved.

For example, psychiatry is presently one of the core groups that is critically involved with mental health, and this group is benefiting from a vogue characterized by labels such as "mental health," "community mental health," "community psychiatry," "social psychiatry," etc. These labels are ideological extensions that are presented in order to increase the probability of obtaining assets. While not yet truly standardized, the latter conceptions include a heavy reliance on what may be termed out-patient therapy, which, in effect, describes much of the current effort, including the community psychiatry proposals. Within this realm, therapy by chemicals and communications are both prominent. The latter, in the form of group or community therapies, attempts to marshal collective pressures and to bring them to bear on deviating individuals. The result is seen as being closer to "suppressive therapy" than to the model of insight therapy cultivated by psychoanalysis. These therapies are close to the strategies associated with social engineering and involve manipulative methods of norm control that are utilized in the nontherapeutic traditions. As these group methods expand, it is predicted that the image of the psychiatrist will merge with those engaged in manipulative strategies, with the tactics of religious institutions, and with the admonitory or indoctrinal programs of other social areas.

In addition, the use of chemicals, which is seen as an appropriate medical-psychiatric role, will also tend to be merged with another series of activities. That is, the use of drugs by the psychiatrist to effect individual behavioral modification does not sharply differentiate him from the traditional doctor of medicine. Thus, the expanding chemical role probably will serve to exaggerate the difference between the somatically oriented and the norm-managing psychiatrist. At the same time, it is anticipated that programs that come under the heading of community mental health are likely to come into direct competition with programs that are justified in terms of leisure, or "wider participation in education and culture," or other similar formulations. Furthermore, it is probably safe to predict that the social and behavioral scientists will gradually be less willing to follow the leadership of the psychiatric wing of medicine, especially when the norm-managing characteristics of the community strategy become more evident. Similarly, the innovations that deal with norm management and cultural process are likely to be supported in the name of ideologies other than that of mental health. More plausible ideologies that are likely to be attractive in the future might be "the cultivation of human resources," "the cultivation of potential manpower," and "cultural reconstruction."

In view of these suppositions, several generalizations were made about public policies toward mental health. One basic objective of public policy is to vindicate the claim of every human being to achieve mental health. Such an objective is recommended because it fits with a series of existing ideologies such as "human dignity," "life, liberty, and the pursuit of happiness," etc. Since mental health implies, not a problem-free life, but a life capable of meeting problems without inner demoralization, people need to have some sort of access to help. It is important to recognize, however, that troubled people may escape from an internal predicament by suppressing any recognition of difficulty and behaving in ways that make them less troublesome to others. Therefore, if an individual is capable of resolving his stresses by joining a nondestructive subculture, he leaves the category of those who are usually viewed or treated as mentally ill. Norm management becomes most important when the range of current mental health and broad social concerns is viewed within a scheme differentiating those who are "troubled" from those who are "troublesome." Attempts at management or solution are much more easily mobilized to deal with the "troublesome" than is the case for those who are merely "troubled." A second generalization is that if the goal of mental health is to be approximated, much less achieved, then the community must have at its disposal a pool of manpower adequately motivated and skilled to identify mental illness and to provide the treatment required to alleviate or cure, while making sure that the sufferer does not have destructive impact upon himself or others.

Discussion centered on the basic societal conflict that exists, as far as public policy is concerned, as attempts are now made to implement the expanded concepts of mental health. In essence, the conflict can be characterized as one between the egalitarian or normative principle and the achievement principle. What has occurred is an attempt to democratize the provision of mental health services and to make them public rather than private properties. Once a service is allocated to, or extended to, the public sector, to which presumably all citizens are supposed to be entitled, adequate mental care becomes as difficult to provide (and as expensive) as adequate medical care, education for all, or equal economic opportunity. The egalitarian norm and the achievement principle are in conflict, since, on the one hand, we express the belief that all citizens should be treated equally, while, on the other, our private enterprise society is one that is intimately tied to the achievement norm, and this norm is usually expressed in terms of differential income. Society is committed to a high degree of differentiation in the allocation of its rewards and in the access to the opportunity structures of society. As we move toward the accomplishment of the principle of egalitarianism, we come face to face with the cost. In order to actually address the problem of providing mental health services to all people, we must be prepared to face a major redistribution of resources in the society.

As long as mental health deals with drug therapies or other individual therapies, it is not threatening to the existing social structures, and, particularly, it is not threatening to free enterprise. Once, however, the problem is seen as the result of an inadequate, unequal, and destructive environment, it becomes a distinct threat to the existing political and economic systems. In this sense Albee's position is very close to Lasswell's, because they both point to the conflict that exists between those who see the mental health problem as essentially one of medicine in the traditional sense and those who approach it from the point of view of family structure, social process, or destructive environments. Viewed from within the microcosm of mental health or the macrocosm of the total society, differential threats to existing political and economic hierarchies will stimulate different resistances to the changes necessary to accomplish these egalitarian goals, as well as to the most effective and/or innovative use of appropriate manpower and economic assets.

In analyzing some of the same issues from an economic point of view, the discussion focused on the proposition that no matter how prosperous a nation may be, resources are scarce relative to wants, and, therefore, no society is ever likely to pursue all of its goals simultaneously. Thus, it is central to understand that to economize is to make a choice. As is true in most noneconomic analyses, the health fields tend to treat priorities as though they were absolutes, whereas the economist treats them as relative functions. For example, prevention and treatment cannot be compared as absolute priorities; rather, they must be considered relative to one another. In the health fields, it is usually stated that it is better to prevent than to treat, but economists would say that this is true only if both approaches are somewhere near the same cost; if one is significantly more costly than the other, it must be asked if this is what is most wanted, because if the option is taken for the costly approach, it is clear that many other things must be given up.

The term "cost" is being used here in the broadest generic sense and is not limited to a consideration of dollars alone. It includes people, resources, and the very structure of society and government that is involved in achieving stated or implied goals. The economist operates in terms of goals, but the goals are set for him by society. Economics and the economic considerations of mental illness and health may be reduced simply to: what is it we would like to do; what is it we wish to give up in order to get something else? This ultimately reflects value judgments, not necessarily questions of efficiency or relative costs.

Although the necessity for stated and measurable goals was highlighted by discussion of economic factors, the lack of specificity of mental health goals, the vagueness of terminology, and the failure to measure effectiveness of effort were ubiquitous throughout. Following the discussion of ideology, it can be readily seen that "improving mental health" is an expression of sentiment, not a meaningful goal for which to specify manpower, programs, or costs. There is no question that the term must be broken down into manageable and specifiable components and goals if rational analysis is to proceed. In the language of the economist, it must be disaggregated. The disaggregation of global mental health objectives into manageable subgoals can lead to more precise specification of manpower needs. On the current national scene, manpower needs, particularly in mental health, imply an inherent assumption of shortage, a term rarely approached and assessed systematically.

A type of economic analysis such as Hanson's internal rate-of-return approach offers considerable manpower information not usually available. In this approach, the rate of return (or interest) is determined for the investment in training in a given occupation and is compared with other occupations. If one rate of return is comparatively high, it *may* indicate that there is a shortage in that category. Actually, the conclusion as to the existence of a shortage is based upon essential qualifications to the method, which can probably best indicate directionality rather than absolute judgments as to manpower shortages or surpluses. Other factors may be prepotent, such as the willingness of society to offer a high rate of return in exchange for ready availability of services (as for physicians or dentists), or possibly because a given group is willing to deal with problems that society would rather not face or deal with. Economists themselves are quick to point out that income alone is not the only factor in such cost-benefit analyses, but that other factors, such as prestige, security, power, status, etc., tend to equalize or balance out income.

Still, the type of information offered by such analyses, coupled with the types of data and analyses available on career and job motivation and choice factors, can lead to increased understanding of the manpower pool and market. It is obvious that any desire to increase a particular manpower segment of the total labor pool involves far more than legislation or job availability. As was pointed out repeatedly during the discussion, the manpower characteristics of a society are part of the total life of that society and can be approached only in that total context.

Although economics was characterized by Carlyle as "the dismal science," this was anything but the case in the discussion of the economics of mental health manpower. The conceptual schemes and methodological points raised within the framework of economics served as an essential focus for translation and linked the social, political, governmental, and medical points of view.

The basic economic proposition—that all social goals cannot be fully pursued simultaneously (although our society, paradoxically, seems to start with the proposition that all social goals *can* be simultaneously pursued)—was the point of departure for consideration of the processes of choice and decision. The essential point was that there are bridges that can be established between economic analyses and what have to be behavioral decisions that affect the allocation of resources. Problems begin to emerge with some clarity only at the point where achievable goals are specified. An analogy was drawn to the space program, where a highly unspecific goal, "to explore outer space," was translated into the very specific and rather attractive goal of "landing a man on the moon." Given a specific and attainable objective, it can be placed on a temporal dimension; systematic assessment of factors such as levels of allocation and resources, program content, and manpower types may be made within the framework of time needed for overall goal achievement.

As Klarman stated, "If you try to pursue a lot of vast goals simultaneously, you will achieve whatever you achieve, but in the process you will be distorting and you may well do one or two things fully, and other things on which you would put a rather high value, you do to a very limited extent. If you do realize limitations and look at policy decisions sequentially, you have a better chance of coming out even at the margins, whatever your evaluation system is."

Since economic analyses utilize data that reflect assessments of costs, benefits (tangible and intangible), outcomes, services, and products, the translation to mental health definitions, concepts, criteria, and research was rather immediate and facile. In all aspects, however, the well-known illusiveness of mental health data was always apparent. The controversy over models and manpower, a contemporary debate exemplified by Albee's paper, served as a conceptual bridge to bring the issues of manpower, politics, and economics into sharp relief.

Albee's basic position is that if the causes of disturbed behavior are unclear, the model of explanation that is in ascendancy dictates the institutions through which services will be offered. He suggests an examination of the ascendant model to determine if it is appropriate and justifiable.

Essentially, he compares two models. The first emphasizes the learning process and focuses on continuity of behavior (e.g., from normal through abnormal). This model stresses prevention and environmental factors, and seeks individual strengths upon which to build. The second emphasizes the organic, biochemical or neurological, and is likely to stress the discontinuity of behavior, and the treatment emphasis is on the discovery of a relatively singular or basic organic cause. It was recognized that these models or approaches are not mutually exclusive. However, the pertinent point is that the dominant illness model is related very closely to the organic approach, and, therefore, it is the illness model that is ascendant. Consequently, the principal institutional approach to treatment is hospitalization and cure; one seeks to change the organic process or at best to rehabilitate after the impact of an organic failure. Once the particular kind of institutional approach has been determined, this in turn specifies the kind of manpower that is needed. Because of this determination, it is claimed that we have no way to solve the manpower shortages; they will remain chronic, since this model requires many more physicians and other medical personnel than are now being trained to replace themselves proportionate to an expanding population.

Albee's plea is that if the social-environmental-learning model were given encouragement and increased political and economic support, it would be possible to deal more effectively with manpower shortages, since this model does not require extremely scarce and expensive manpower. It would be possible to train people at the bachelor's-degree level to deliver many of the needed services.

Discussions of models of man and his functioning provide stimulating interchange, but the issues Albee raises are only partially those of knowledge and its application as related to types of manpower. The crux of the argument is one of power and authority. The maintenance of a medical power structure inhibits maximum service delivery via other types of persons and agencies. Furthermore, despite its basic organic orientation, medicine is not as reductionistic as is often claimed, and all of medicine is in some significant way dependent upon concepts of behavior. Social-learning-environmental considerations are increasingly evident in psychiatric as well as medical practice. However, the introduction of behavioral concepts is something of a mixed blessing, since the very medical people who should be furthering biomedical organic hypotheses and research have all too often been subverted into an increasingly pervasive socioenvironmental model incorporated, however, into a medical political structure. It is not possible (or desirable) to separate medicine, either as a science or as a political system, from psychopathology or vice versa. The issue is one of boundaries to the expansive concepts of psychopathology and the sharing and coordinating of authority, jurisdiction, and power along more socially realistic lines.

In considering more appropriate division of labor for the delivery of services, which is the ultimate purpose of manpower, it is apparent that the particular models or types of manpower are of critical importance only when the political and economic factors are resolved, since these factors are the media through which social philosophy or ideology is implemented.

Serious mental conditions are chronic and resist change, and, therefore, must be treated largely within tax-supported agencies rather than through the usual private-practice, free-enterprise system that characterizes most of medicine's delivery of service. The disparity that exists between those services available and offered to upper and lower classes is not merely a matter of models (although this is a major factor) ; more fundamentally, it relates to the economic-political system and the prevailing achievement norm mentioned earlier. It was not demonstrated that these problems would be resolved by taking responsibility away from medicine and providing it to other professional groups. There was no question that overemphasis and reliance upon illness concepts inhibit maximum return at this stage, but the nature of the social ills now viewed as contributory to mental ill-health goes right to the heart of our economic-political system; and manpower issues per se become relatively insignificant in contrast.

It is upon these issues that the ideas of Lasswell, Klarman, and Albee may be integrated. In the health field there is a vast body of knowledge, but there is not yet a powerful integrating model. In the absence of this master design, it is essential to keep as many models (options) viable as is possible until careful research or significant experience indicates which of these are not useful.

The lack of availability of a singular, integrative theory was not the only reason given for favoring a plurality of equally nurtured models. Also directly pertinent are the arguments presented from the economic and political points of view emphasizing the need for subgoals rather than aggregate approaches. It is highly probable that many of the subgoals will necessitate different approaches (models) as well as differing structures, agencies, and manpower. This point is highlighted by the caution offered by Lasswell that objectives explicitly related to mental health must be distinguished from other goals that only affect mental health. When only global objectives, such as "improving the mental health of the nation," are specified, then almost any problem of the human condition may be attributed to mental ill-health, and the mental health fields are burdened (whether willingly or not) with an implicit promise to "cure" or alleviate all the ills of society.

In emphasizing the broad conceptual and theoretical issues of manpower, there was at times a lack of emphasis on the very real and pressing pragmatic problems. It remained for Miller and Wexler to make explicit the fundamental contrasts between theory and practice, and to express the sense of frustration experienced when theoretical conceptions do not reach to the needs of service programs that must operate from a pragmatic base. Specifically, Lasswell's prediction of the recesssion of the ideology of mental health was questioned. From the point of view of a large state agency, it appears that mental health has been forced to continuously enlarge its scope by virtue of the added demands from the public and federal agencies to include more human problems and to provide services for more people. From the practical standpoint, it seems clear that in order to provide even basic services to the mentally ill, it has been and still is necessary to continuously broaden the purview of the operating agency. This is true, first, because so many more aspects of human life and society have been recognized as impinging upon this domain, and, second, because other fields and agencies have not attempted to grapple with the issues involved. One of the practical problems of a government agency is that it must continually reach out for additional tasks and support, even if only to remain visible to the legislative and executive budgetary processes. If it remains marginal, the agency will not be able to adequately perform any portion of its assigned task. Specifically for the state agency, it means that the quality of care for the mentally ill and mentally retarded must be continuously improved: the teaching of those who work in the field, the quality of research that is involved, and the information that the public should have—all become involved merely to discharge the original task. Since a government agency is assigned definite responsibilities, it becomes mandatory to be intrusive in the quality of training and the production of manpower in mental health.

In order for an agency to discharge these responsibilities and to improve the managerial, administrative, and social systems by means of which services are delivered, it is clear that these efforts go beyond any model formulation that has been presented. The kinds of considerations and activities involved in the creation of meaningful roles and jobs for new, innovative types of workers offer an example of the kind of extension of responsibility that seems unavoidable on the practical level. In order to minimize personnel difficulties, positions must be attractive for recruitment and retention, tasks meaningful and satisfying, educational background and occupational skills specified, and career ladders developed. In far too many of the efforts to develop new and innovative mental health jobs and roles, these factors have been ignored. On the other hand, these factors go well beyond the direct care and treatment that constitute a mental health agency's primary mandate. They are, however, critical in order to insure the stable and competent labor force upon which the primary objective rests. The mental health agency thus becomes involved in broad-scale personnel and labor-force issues, educational standards and competence, continuing education, etc.

Although these extensions of activity and responsibility have been undertaken to maximize primary mental health efforts, they are dubious blessings. Scarce professional manpower becomes involved, resources are spread more thinly, and the net effect is a dilution of primary effort and effect, despite the laudable motivations. Rather than continuation of this pattern, without visible end, pressure must be brought to bear upon and support given to the development and expansion of the components of society and/or government that are more appropriate and often more competent to discharge these obligations and functions.

The pressures that compel mental health agencies to enter such a diversity of activities are not all external to the fields themselves. In the effort to develop new types of mental health workers, the rigidity of the jurisdictional lines of the existing professional groups also presents serious problems. At times it seems that these rigidities require workers in other areas or new kinds of personnel to be absorbed and controlled so as not to interfere with existing professional prerogatives.

Consider, for example, the mental health professional's relationship to the foster parent. Foster parents presumably have a potentially stable, identifiable role—that of being a parent. However, many mental health professionals tend to see the foster parent as an assistant social worker and thus attempt to impose on him a social treatment rather than a parent role. Foster parents should be specialists in "parenting," not in child development or deviancy.

The same kind of problem was seen as often implicit in current thinking about comprehensive community mental health centers. There is some evidence at the local level that such centers seek to induce new measures of control in a way similar to the example of the social worker and the parent. This tends to focus on the control of community resources in the service of mental health rather than on the development and strengthening of independent community resources. The conclusion drawn was that as the mental health fields move toward the use of other kinds of personnel and become more engaged with other community agencies, it would be better to view such people or agencies as independently functioning entities and autonomous specialists.

It was also specified that interacting on an equal footing with other professions and agencies that deal with human health and welfare was mandatory if the problem areas of mental health were to be placed in a more reasonable perspective. The pragmatics of the delivery of services and the administration of mental health agencies emerged as the common ground where the need for "disaggregation," specification of subgoals, delineation of responsibilities, and utilization of plural models became clear.

From the totality of the discussions and the formal papers, it was possible to extract a set of general principles, criticisms, and/or recommendations regarding the mental health manpower field. These following points, while not necessarily mutually exclusive or exhaustive in scope, are seen as essentials to be dealt with in order to utilize manpower in a systematic, maximally productive fashion:

1. The boundaries and definition of the problems are too gross, indicating a need both for a contraction in the scope of endeavor and for specification of subgoals.

2. There is an absolute necessity to adopt a set of operational specifications for subgoal outcomes with which the field is to be concerned. This could lead to exploration of the minimum training (programs) that would elicit the personnel who would contribute most to these outcomes.

3. There has been a relative absence of selection of critical elements in the field. Thus, there has been a built-in problem of obsolescence in education and training relative to functions.

4. For many aspects of behavior, direct frontal attacks may well be self-defeating. Careful analyses show that different approaches focused on various aspects of the total ecology by multiple groups and agencies offer ultimate maximum mental health gains. The relationship to mental health of these other approaches needs to be carefully articulated.

5. There is a critical need for training more research people, since it is obvious that there still remain far too many questions posed on researchable issues for which data are not available.

6. In order for theory to be utilized maximally, the questions posed must be sharpened, outcomes specified, and benefits measured.

7. By starting at the point of specifying services to be delivered and functions to be performed, one might free oneself from preconceptions as to how they can be accomplished and by whom. Hopefully, this offers access to other kinds of manpower supplies that are now lost or neglected.

8. There are multiple approaches to and definitions of the manpower terms "need," "supply," "demand," and "shortages." Approaches, however, do exist in which each of these terms can be translated from vague statements of social philosophy into measurable, researchable criteria based upon specific tasks, functions, personnel, and outcomes. This remains largely undone for mental health endeavors.

Index